Celebrate 2000

Catch the Millennium Bug with Eric and Young Writers

KENT

Edited by Dave Thomas

First published in Great Britain in 1999 by
YOUNG WRITERS
Remus House,
Coltsfoot Drive,
Woodston,
Peterborough, PE2 9JX
Telephone (01733) 890066

All Rights Reserved

Copyright Contributors 1999

HB ISBN 0 75431 634 3
SB ISBN 0 75431 635 1

FOREWORD

Young Writers have produced poetry books in conjunction with schools for over eight years; providing a platform for talented young people to shine. This year, the Celebration 2000 collection of regional anthologies were developed with the millennium in mind.

With the nation taking stock of how far we have come, and reflecting on what we want to achieve in the future, our anthologies give a vivid insight into the thoughts and experiences of the younger generation.

We were once again impressed with the quality and attention to detail of every entry received and hope you will enjoy the poems we have decided to feature in *Celebration 2000 Kent* for many years to come.

Contents

Barry Grimes	1

Anthony Roper CP School

Benjamin Eliot Newton	2
Craig Lewis Farrell	3
Adam Reardon	4
Robert Fever	5
Louise Giannoni	6
Gina Tse	7
Lewis Kateley	8
Alex Frankson	9
Peter Leonard Sutton	10
Tom Watling	11
Luke Berwick	12
Hugh Davis	13
Sebastien Rousset	14
Charles Minshaw	15
Drew Bennett	16
Peter Clarke	17
Samantha Watts	18
Matthew Bray	19
Hannah Marie Cuthbertson	20
Emma Stacy	21
James Wiles	22
Hadleigh Wiles	24

Brenzett CE Primary School

Laura Wilcoxon	25
Samantha Frith	26
Harriet Gurr	26
Jessica Martin	27
David Carnell	27
Emma Louise Keerie	28
Sarah Richardson	28
Jayde Wren	29
Daniel Clark	29

Benjamin Wyatt	30
Peter Pike	30
Becky Clark	31
Alan Morris	31
Caroline Grimaldi	32
Bethany Dearlove	32
Nicola Watts	33
Aspen Wren	34
Steven Jones	34
Benedict Standen	35
Victoria Richardson	35
Callum John Mann	36
Chantelle Washford	36
Felix Brason	37

Chiddingstone CE Primary School

Amy Banyon	37
John Cackett	38
Ellie Harris	38
James Pickard-Eastwood	39
Nancy Goldman-Edwards	39
Kalyani McCarthy	40
Ellen Matkins	41
Finlay Robertson	41
Louise Robinson	42
Timothy Corby	42
Daniel Weeks	43
William Mayes	44
Louise Cackett	44
Zoë Quirk	45
Andrew Lucas	46
Nicholas Hards	46

Days Lane Primary School

Becky Stanley, Megan Roberts, Daley Bibby, Victoria Castle, Nicola Ward, Laura Allen, Sian English & Michelle Jermin	47
Hollie Lawrence & Chanelle Handley	48

Sarah Henry & Sara Kenney	48
Alex Pankhurst	49
Daniel Haley	49
Sophie Durham	50
Mitchell Murrell & Graham Hawley	50
Luke Fenn	51

East Stour CP School

Katherine Ritchie	52
Stuart Conochie	52
David Phillips	52
Kirsty Olson	53
Emma Turner	53
Kaylie Russell	53
Abigail Ireland	54
Karina Sturch	55
Gemma Lincoln	55
Louise Weeden	56
Lauren Mackelborough	56
Jenni Steele	56
Katherine Pitt	57
Kate Collingridge	57
Karly Medcalf	57

Egerton CE Primary School

Kaylie Cairns	58
Scarlett Atkins	58
James Alexander Cox	59
Cameron Forbes	60
Katrina Saunders	60
Arnold Duncan	61
Christopher Holmes	61
Alexa Jay Craven	62
Holly Atkins	62
Kit Rowe	63
Charlotte Button	64
Charlotte Manning	64
Ben Madden	65

Harriet Adams	65
Charlotte Dray	66
Laura Filmer	66

Friars School

Oliver Hill	67
David Leavey	67
Nikhil Sanyal	68
Lee Barrett	69
Joe Ottaway	69
Stefan Pfefferlé	70
Nicholas Schatunowski	70
Mark Ashley	71
William Fletcher	71
James Loudon	72
Rosie Ransley	72
Rebecca Startin	73
Tom Elias	74
Alex Smith	74
Tristan Spencer	75
Christopher Plowman	76
Benedict Bunyard	76
Adam Bushell	77
Joseph Price	77
Edward Edmondson	78
Emma Cragg	79
Damien Bailey	80
Sebastian Goodwin-Day	80
Sarah Haselup	81

Great Chart School

Hannah Hogben & Becky Bell	82
Lance Johnson	82
Adam Wilkinson	83
Rhiannon Simmons & Abigail Ennis	83
Richard Lyne	84
Hazel Crisp & Jennifer Keen	84
Thomas Bushnell & Ben Moffat	85

James Barden & Matthew Mansfield	85
Sam Yates	86
Cara Jane Shearing	86
Robert Iles	87
Abby Jones	87
Jennifer Keen, Hazel Crisp & Emily Ford	87
Kirstie Leigh Atkins	88
Hollie Weatherill & Katie Parish	88
Jason Stewart	89
Samantha Bacon	89
Emily Ford	90
Becky Bell & Felicity Pentland	90
Abigail Ennis	90
Lisette Priestley	91

Harcourt Primary School

Gary Jackson	91
Neil Andrews	92
Alistair Buchanan	92
Nicholas Phillipps	92
Sarah Browne	93
Joshua Graves	93
Terri Rees	93
Claire Orchard	94
Chelsey Atkins	94
Adam Eccles	95
Oliver Simpson	95
Carly-Anne Dowsett	96
Bethia Coady-Mayall	97
Ross Godden	97
Robert Jenner	98
Leasha Donnelly	98
Jacob Coady-Mayall	99
Jasmin Louise Cowdroy	100
Warren Denman	101
Natasha Stitson	101
Rachael Martin	102
Lisa Wilson	103

Danny Richmond	104
Harold Arnold	105
Ashley Wells	105
Christiana Cridland	106
Sarah Louise Bliss	106
Charlotte Lund	107
Daniel Howarth	108
Dean Richmond	109
Daisy Fordham	109

Hextable Junior School

Megan Morris	110
Kathryn Sutton	110
Ben Lawrence	111
Aaron Farmer	111
Ben Nazarjuk	112
Lynsey White	112
Sian Birleson	113
Emma Kirby	114
Natalie Clough	115
Carly Fordham	116
Craig Strachan	116
Aaron Cook	117
Rosemary Haward	118
Nathan Morris	118
Gemma Chuter	119
James Wyatt	120
Richard Brown	120
Emma Hamilton-Jenkins	121
Sachin Wadher	122
Robert Bennett	122
Rebecca Carpenter	123
Darrell Baker	124
Sam Luchford	124
Nick Self	125
James Culliford	126
Michaela Read	126
Chloe Smithers	127

Lauren Evans	127
Charlotte Phillips	128
Adam Draper	128
James Tuffee	129
Rachel Mole	129
Rachel Parker	130
George Hutchins	130
Sarah Crouch	131
Debbie Stoner	132
Martyn Searles	133
Christina Monti	134
Ben Samuel	134
Philip Donkersley	135
Joe Sandford	135
Edele Barnett	136
Bradley Freeman	136
Alex Ward	137
Jade Wright	137
Jeb Lynch	138
Christopher Blanchard	138
Amelia Bushell	139
Ricky Bullimore	139

Knockholt CE Primary School

Karina Cork	140
Callum McDonald	140
Arron Smart	141
Kate Morris	141
Lorna Tester	142
Ellie Fay Gatsell	142
Tom Hinks	143
Gemma Cakebread	143
Katie Gettins	144
Samuel Shaw	144
Rosie Kelly	144
Christopher Cheeseman	145
Suki Marie Clark	145
Charles Robson	146

Jessica Ann Gibbons	146
Laura Copeland	146
Matthew Shackleton	147
Chad Williams	147

Lancelot Primary School

Liesel Cleaver	148
Dalia Awad	149
Scott Hazle	149
Jenna Ganney	150
Sara McDermott	150

Merton Court School

Gareth Taylor	151
Billy Thurston	151
Lauren Everson	152
David Williamson	152
Amit Patel	153
Katy Davies	153
Francesca Mestre	154
Jason Macdonald	154
Hannah Jarmyn	155
Bhavin Pandya	156
Laurie Clode	156

Mundella CP School

Jody-Lan Castle	157
Simon Stuart	157
Lauren Staveley	158
Joe Chambers	158
Michael Ward	159
Gemma Atkins	159
Daniel Bail	160
Natasha Spearpoint	160
Kirk Beasley	161
Joshua Johnson	161

Northbourne Park School
- Alex Bragg — 161
- Aaron Kent — 162
- Oliver Ford — 162
- Theo Dunay — 163
- Richard Gould — 164
- Daniel Hurley — 164
- Susannah Fox — 165
- James Stiles — 166
- Edward Barker — 166
- Jack Lambert — 167
- Elizabeth Ferrar — 167
- Samantha Jones — 168
- Adam Pickett — 168
- Robin Bailey — 169

St Andrew's Preparatory School, Edenbridge
- James A Sinclair — 170
- Emily Hart — 170
- Helen Ritchie — 171
- Joshua Kaufmann — 172
- Phillippa Woolard — 172
- Glenn Masson — 173
- Rachel Pickford — 174
- Rose Hunnam — 174
- Georgina Wells — 175
- Lauren Prewer — 176
- Lewis Noble — 176
- Tom Jennings — 177
- Seán Hickey — 178
- Milton Cato — 178
- Sophie Armitage — 179
- Henry Croft — 180

St Eanswythe School, Folkstone
- Siän Bolton — 180
- Chantelle Marsh — 181
- Josie Bryant — 182

Terri Hines	183
Jade Underdown	184
Devi Patel	184
Christopher Croucher	185
Charles Brisley	186
Patricia Plested	187

St Ronan's School, Hawkhurst

Charles Henry Player	187
James Merewether	188
Michelle Faure	188
Alexander Graham	189
Rupert Tozer	189
Anthony Drewe	190
Jonathan Langer	190
Edward Prest	191
Tom Helm	192
Richard Blundell	192
Donal MacCrann	193
Harry Hoblyn	194
Alex Kelin	194
Geoffrey Woodman	195
Oliver Marshall	195
Ralph Johnson	196
Andrew Denman	196
Charlie Houghton	197
Jonathan Clowes	197
Bertie Blundell	198
James Duval	198
Alexander Macintyre	199
Alastair Borland	200
Phoebe Katis	200
Rupert Munro-Faure	201
Sarah Yelland	201
William Prest	201
Toby Walker	202
Oliver Tozer	202
Anna Munro-Faure	203

Victoria Yelland	203
Jack Stow	203
Charlie Elias	204

Sandown CP School

Samantha Miles	205
Rebecca Crutchley	205
Matthew Larkins	206
Sonia Woolls	206
Phillipa Engels	207
Ben Kelly	207
Jane Houldsworth	208
Thomas Beach	208
Sophie Barrow	209
Steven Curry	209
Sam Richards	210
Maria Letts	210
Alex Riley	211
Daniel Stenhouse	211
Sam Hutchings	212
Tim Pitcher	212
Joseph Douglas	213
Neil Jackson	214
Holly Newing	214
Simon Love	215
Emma Lawless	215
Ben Stevens	216
Cai Martin	216
Matthew Robinson	217
Jon Stones	217
Vicky Smith	218
Thomas Best	218
Laura Skelton	219
Hannah Gearey	220
Lisa Owen	220

The Poems

THE STREAMY RIVER

The river bends,
It also tends
To have a lot of fish in it.

The river's wet
And you will get
The same if you climb into it.

The source of a river starts in a cave
And about it explorers rave.

There's a Roman villa
Right next to a river,
There's also a bridge and some fields.

The River Thames
Can sparkle like gems,
But also it can look quite dull.

A people-carrier
Hit the Thames barrier,
And also cost a lot of money.

Barry Grimes (10)

CELEBRATION 2000

Electronic tutors
and mobile schools.
Digital libraries
and swimming pools.
How will we move
and what will we do?
During the millennium
will I still know you?
Will robots turn on
to bake you some bread?
Or will they deliver
on an old moped?
Computers whiz and beep
as they print your work.
But then they start to sound
a little bit berserk.
Will this be the millennium?
As robots prowl the streets
and drive along the roads
as they're looking for treats.
People playing music
out of their ear
In the millennium there's nothing
that they can fear.
Hover cars and solar trains
electric planes and wind-powered bikes.
Fusion-powered buses
and small water trikes.
Will *this* be the millennium?
Who knows!

Benjamin Eliot Newton (11)
Anthony Roper CP School

CELEBRATION 2000

Millennium Dome with big celebrations,
Can we all cope with the great temptations?
Will there be trains?
Will there be planes?
The Millennium Dome.

> Will you be able to live on the moon?
> Who knows, it might happen soon,
> Flying into space,
> To another deadly place,
> The Millennium Dome.

Will there be teaching?
Will there be shopping?
Will there be cars?
Will there be bikes?
The Millennium Dome.

> Will there be razors?
> Will there be lasers?
> Will all the fashion change?
> Will we all look very strange?
> The Millennium Dome.

Will we all watch TV?
Or will they be history?
Nobody will know,
Until the great day,
The Millennium Dome.

> Will there be sport?
> Will we all have a passport?
> Nobody will know,
> Until the year 2000,
> The Millennium Dome.

Craig Lewis Farrell (10)
Anthony Roper CP School

Celebration 2000

On the 31st of December,
The month after November,
London's Big Ben,
Will strike 2 hours past 10.
In the next year computers will read 00
And this will cause them to lose everything they have been taught.
People are planning visits to the Millennium Dome,
But the next century will bring disasters unknown.
Spaceships, solar power and contact with outer space,
Life is moving on for the human race.

Fashions and clothes are getting better,
What will they think of next, the flying letter?
Satellite, Cable, Digital, Sky,
All this choice and I don't know why.
I was quite content with channels 1 to 4,
So why these others, I'm not too sure.
The Millennium Bug is thought to harm computers,
But if not will they be our tutors?
Spaceships, solar power and contact with outer space,
Life is moving on for the human race.

Will measurements be new?
Will cows still say 'moo'?
Will the world be a mess?
How will we dress?
What will happen?
Will we have rations?
All of these questions I do not know,
We will just have to wait and see how it goes.
Spaceships, solar power and contact with outer space,
Life is moving on for the human race.

Adam Reardon (10)
Anthony Roper CP School

CELEBRATION 2000

Holidays, parties, raves, dances,
Everybody always prances!
Sit down, relax, have a mug
For here comes the Millennium Bug!

> Ding, dong goes Big Ben,
> Yehah! Shout all men
> Don't sit around acting like a slug
> For here comes the Millennium Bug!

Little green men might come to stay,
Just let them, we will say.
All gather round and please come
And celebrate the millennium.

> Solar-powered cars will roam the streets,
> Everyone will take great feats.
> Let's not drop the momentum
> And celebrate the millennium!

Let's look back on the past year,
And then let's drink lots of beer!
I think I'm really gonna burst
Unless I get to Jan the first!

> Fashion in clothes might change a lot,
> Or clothes will shrivel up and rot!
> I think I need to see the nurse,
> Unless I get to Jan the first!

Will we be cloned and look the same?
And will we all have just one name?
Everyone will be around
To celebrate the year *2000!*

Robert Fever (11)
Anthony Roper CP School

CELEBRATION 2000

Here it comes the Millennium Bug,
Will we all go down the plug!
I'd much rather be at home
Than be stuck in the Millennium Dome.
Here comes the millennium!

Aeroplanes could fall out of the sky
Without bread the birds may die
Salt and petrol could be rationed
I wonder what will be in fashion
Here comes the millennium!

All the traffic may grind to a stop
And all computers may go pop
The church bells may never ring
What will the millennium bring?
Here comes the millennium!

Everyone will celebrate
Will the atmosphere be great?
Pop stars fighting to be number one
Partying till the rising sun.
Here comes the millennium!

We don't have to go to school.
Everyone will think it's cool!
Adults, drinking wine and beer
To celebrate the New Year.

Here comes the millennium!

Louise Giannoni (10)
Anthony Roper CP School

CELEBRATION 2000

Will we use outer space?
That will be a change to the human race!
Will we fly round and round?
Or not even touch the ground!
Will we live on the moon?
I hope that will happen very soon!
Celebration 2000.

Computers are the future,
But will they become our tutor?
Will computers be small?
Or will they not be here at all?
Will the bug scare us all?
It's really dangerous but really small.
Celebration 2000.

The Millennium Dome,
Is like a new home.
The Stone Age, the Romans are from the past,
They have gone away very fast.
The future with lots in store,
Inventions, time travel and lots more!
Celebration 2000.

Lots of people, very happy.
With the millennium round the corner.
Lots of children, very merry
Friends come and party,
Lots of people at home
Are planning to visit the Dome.
Celebration 2000, the millennium!

Gina Tse (10)
Anthony Roper CP School

CELEBRATION 2000

2000 is here,
So celebrate, have a beer.
When you're sitting warm at home
Men are building the Millennium Dome.
Many people having a party,
2000, 2000.

Big Ben, getting ready to ring,
So have a party, have a sing.
Many people look at the time,
Anticipating when Ben will chime.
Many people having a party,
2000, 2000.

12pm will be here soon,
2000, will we live on the moon?
Think of all the electric things,
Will humans develop wings?
Many people having a party,
2000, 2000.

Will we have electric cars?
Will we be friends with beings from Mars?
I cannot wait,
2001 is far too late.
Many people having a party,
2000, 2000.

2000 has been
After all the guests we need a good clean.
While you're having a clean at home
Men are exhibiting the Millennium Dome.
Many people had a party,
2000, 2000.

Lewis Kateley (10)
Anthony Roper CP School

CELEBRATION 2000

Big Ben will strike at twelve midnight,
For the year 2000,
The fireworks, cor what a wonderful sight!
Millennium.

Everyone will cheer aloud,
For the year 2000,
Especially all the wild crowd,
Millennium.

Will there be any more disasters
For the year 2000?
Will people still be covered in plasters?
Millennium.

The Millennium Dome will be a great success,
For the year 2000,
If not, I won't be very impressed,
Millennium.

It will be the biggest party ever,
For the year 2000,
People won't cheer, no, never,
Millennium.

I hope the cars will be improved
For the year 2000
And the rest will be removed
Millennium.

Holidays are booked everywhere
For the year 2000.
Wow! Two seconds to go and here's the town's mayor,
Millennium.

Alex Frankson (11)
Anthony Roper CP School

CELEBRATION 2000

What will happen at the millennium?

How will we get to the Millennium Dome?
Will we be able to see it at home?
I wonder if computers go haywire,
or will they all set on fire?

What will happen at the millennium?

Will we still have cars and trains,
or will we be floating in mini planes?

What will happen at the millennium?

Will we ever get off our chair?
Will we grow really long hair?
Will we have little computerised screens
and will we be eating genetically modified beans?

What will happen at the millennium?

Will there be some school?
Will there be none at all?
Will we still have lots of teachers
or will we have computers with many features?

What will happen at the millennium?

Will we ever live on the moon?
Perhaps it may be very soon.
With spaceships shooting into space,
they now are all over the place.

What will happen at the millennium?

Will we have still the common pound,
or will that be not around?
Or will we have the brand new Euro,
or will we have no money and be down to zero?

Peter Leonard Sutton (11)
Anthony Roper CP School

CELEBRATION 2000

What will happen about the Millennium Bug?
Will it cause us to pull the plug?
When the millennium is finally here
Everyone will drink, shout and cheer.
Celebration 2000.

The only thing I'm worried about,
My computer might go *kaput*.
I can't wait until next year,
I haven't really got anything to fear.
Celebration 2000.

I can't wait until Big Ben goes *dong*,
It's only next year I won't have to wait long.
All your family will get together,
We'll all have fun no matter the weather.
Celebration 2000.

I can't wait until next year,
Hopefully it will not bring a tear.
Next year will be really flash,
Let's hope the bug doesn't cost a lot of cash.
Celebration 2000.

Tom Watling (11)
Anthony Roper CP School

CELEBRATION 2000

Floating cars and talk to mobile phones
Will the computer bug wipe out all our loans?
Will we ever live in space
Or buy a chemical to change our face?
Watch out technology's coming our way!

Will school work be changed to computers?
Will we need a teacher tutor?
Will toys still be cricket bats
Or will they be computerised walking CDs?
Watch out technology's coming our way!

Could there be pocket-sized PCs
Or big home stereo TVs?
Will cars only be solar power?
What about a car with a shower?
Watch out technology's coming our way!

Will there be funny hairstyles?
Will there be tramlines running for miles?
Will lorries be turned into luxury homes?
What are they going to do to the Dome?
Watch out technology's coming our way!

Could there be automatic robots?
Will there be electronic baby cots?
Will we communicate with Pluto?
Will technology change a theatre show?
Watch out technology's coming our way!

Will fashion change a little bit?
Will there be different sports kit?
Will shoes be more technical?
Will there be cameras in the wall?
Watch out technology's coming our way!

Luke Berwick (11)
Anthony Roper CP School

CELEBRATION 2000

Will we play sport?
How will we be taught?
Will we have cars?
Will we live on Mars?
Questions for the millennium.

        Will we have trains?
        What about boats or planes?
        How will we eat?
        Who might we meet?
        Questions for the millennium.

Will we get contact to outer space?
Will I still live with the human race?
Will we all use solar power?
Will we still have the minute and hour?
Questions for the millennium.

        Will we still go to school?
        Or will there be computers for us all?
        Will we have better technology?
        Will we have virtual reality?
        Questions for the millennium.

Will we still have music to listen to?
Will there be cures for every flu?
Will we still watch TV?
Will computers be history?
Questions for the millennium.

        Will all my questions be answered?
        I really wonder if they could?
        Will humans be able to fly?
        Will the millennium just fly by?
        Questions for the millennium.

Hugh Davis (11)
Anthony Roper CP School

Millennium

Party, party all over the place,
People with smiles all over their face.
Everyone was waiting for twelve to arrive,
All were happy to be alive.

Glasses clinking, party poppers popping,
People jumping, skipping and bopping.
Friends all catching buses to see,
Just how important the millennium would be.

The traffic is heavy, we're starting to moan,
But look straight ahead . . . the Millennium Dome.
Vast and white with spheres to the sky,
I'm so happy I feel I could cry.

We start on the tour, can't believe our eyes,
It's enormous, it's grand, it's massive inside.
We see things, we hear things, we smell and we touch,
Thanks Tony Blair we love it so much.

These are the questions that were asked,
Will we live on planet Mars?
What will the fashion be and what will we wear?
Will the new cars be flying through the air?

The Millennium Dome was too good to believe,
But all too soon it was time to leave,
I really loved my tour of the Dome,
I wish so much it could be my home.

Twelve was going to strike any time
That very same moment, Big Ben chimed
Everyone celebrated, they knew this was 'it'
And everyone sang Robbie Williams' greatest hit.

Millennium!

Sebastien Rousset (11)
Anthony Roper CP School

CELEBRATION 2000

When the year 2000 is finally here,
Everyone will be having fun.
They stay up late drinking beer,
Until the millennium is here.
Celebration 2000.

The only problem with the millennium would be,
There's a Millennium Bug which is here in a dash.
Computers, lights and electricity,
The Millennium Bug is doing it in a flash.
Celebration 2000.

What will happen in this new year?
Robots, dinosaurs, even tonnes of snow.
Could come to this world and give us fear
All this could happen, we don't know.
Celebration 2000.

I can't wait until next year.
Hopefully it will not bring a tear.
Next year will be really flash,
let's hope the bug doesn't cost cash.
Celebration 2000.

Charles Minshaw (10)
Anthony Roper CP School

CELEBRATION 2000

We got in our car
And followed a star
Right to the Millennium Dome.
It is a huge dome,
Made out of glass,
With steel structures of fibreglass.
Thoughts went through my head,
Most of them I started to dread.
What if the lights go out?
One, two, three as I count.
One single wire,
Could make the place go haywire.
Some more thoughts went through my head,
Like a pencil without a lead.
Don't stay in, go out late,
Go out clubbing with your mates.
Big Ben could blow up,
Or the Queen's china cups.
What if someone's on a plane
And it's going as slow as a crane?
Say, for instance, I fly to Perth,
And a meteor hits the Earth.
What will I do if I get hit?
I don't know I'll have to wait for it.
I'm building up my adrenaline,
For the millennium.
It's almost here,
And I'm full of cheer.

Drew Bennett (10)
Anthony Roper CP School

CELEBRATION 2000

Big Ben strikes twelve!
Cheers ring out, to greet a new beginning.
All around people are dancing and singing!
Millennium fever!

Two thousand years have gone,
Since the birth of God's only Son!
Millennium fever!

The whole world is celebrating,
A brighter future stands in waiting!
Millennium fever!

The Millennium Dome's exhibitions are vast,
Showing achievements from centuries past!
Millennium fever!

Computer systems make modern life hum,
Will all these go wrong in the millennium?
Millennium fever!

Stores may empty, businesses down the plug,
All because of the Millennium Bug!
Millennium fever!

Life in outer space,
Will that be another place?
Millennium fever!

A space station being lived on by an astronaut
Maybe time travel back to the year nought!
Millennium fever!

Partying up and down the UK
Some may even say,
'Millennium fever'.

Peter Clarke (10)
Anthony Roper CP School

CELEBRATION 2000

Celebration 2000,
what shall I do?
Will things be the same,
or will they be new?
I wonder if the world will change?
I'm not sure, will it be strange?
Millennium 2000

The first baby born on millennium day,
will it be famous? What will they say?
Will it become a big superstar?
When it is older, will it get a new car?
Millennium 2000.

The Millennium Bug, destroying computers,
and out on the road bibbing our hooters.
Around the world and living in space.
How will it dominate the whole human race?
Millennium 2000

At present we travel by car, train and plane
will there be rockets or more of the same?
Don't forget the great British fuel,
what will they use instead of this tool?
Millennium 2000

Will I have to go to school?
I'm not so sure, but it's the rule!
Will I learn through the *Internet*?
I hope I do, but I haven't yet!
Millennium 2000.

Samantha Watts (11)
Anthony Roper CP School

CELEBRATION 2000

The millennium is coming,
And we'll be decorating.
When the clock strikes 12,
We will be celebrating.

        The millennium is coming,
        A celebration in the Dome.
        I will not be there,
        I'll have a party at home.

The millennium is coming,
I wonder what will change?
Will we still drink Coca-Cola?
Will eggs still be free range?

        The millennium is coming,
        Will we still play sport?
        Will there be an offside rule?
        Will PE still be taught?

The millennium is coming,
It's not that far away.
Will we have cars?
Will we still have a holiday?

        The millennium is coming,
        Will fashion be the same?
        Will people wear different clothes?
        Will people dress in shame?

The millennium is coming,
I wish the time would come.
But once it has started,
I know it will be gone.

Matthew Bray (11)
Anthony Roper CP School

CELEBRATION 2000

Why does it cause so much trouble?
Can't it just fly away.
I hope it doesn't double,
Or it will be a disaster.
Oh Millennium Bug, get lost.
      I can't wait.

Will there be solar power cars?
Will there be electric cars?
Or will there be boring fuel?
I hope we have solar powered,
Because electric's expensive.
      I can't wait.

Questions, questions, questions,
Will there be tiny computers?
By now we should be in space.
Technology is an amazing race,
It's growing every minute.
      I can't wait.

Maybe it will contain clowns,
I wonder if people will go there.
They say it will be expensive,
But what I really want to know is . . .
What will be in this thing?
      I can't wait.

Crackers, cookies, parties are great!
I hope I will not be late.
Big Ben strikes any minute now,
Made it - 5, 4, 3, 2, 1.
Ding dong, bing bong, ding dong, bing bong.
      I can't wait.

Hannah Marie Cuthbertson (11)
Anthony Roper CP School

CELEBRATION 2000

In the millennium will there be
Small computers for just the eye to see?
We might even go out and live in space
And find an alien that leaves with no trace
      In the new millennium

We might have cinemas in our own home
I wonder what it's like in the Millennium Dome?
I wonder what schools will be like
There may be another war where girls fight
      In the new millennium

We'll have a party and have lots of fun
And we could eat nice chocolate buns
I'll stay up all night to hear the clock chime
Then after that I'll have a great time
      In the new millennium

I wonder what sort of cars we will have
We might even have floating cabs
We could have robots that do our chores
They could tidy up mess and clean floors
      In the new millennium

What will the Millennium Bug do?
It could do things to make us look like a fool
Perhaps the fashions may even change
We might wear silver and look rather strange
      In the new millennium

I wonder if cars will have solar power
There may be foods which taste rather sour
Whatever happens I'll remember the past
With all the things ahead it could be a task
      In the new millennium.

Emma Stacy (11)
Anthony Roper CP School

CELEBRATION 2000

The Millennium Dome has been built,
Hopefully not on the tilt.
Year 2000.

The clock will strike 12.01,
And the millennium is to come.
Year 2000.

Will all the lights go out
Whilst all the world spins about?
Year 2000.

We might have future technology,
With cars and new biology.
Year 2000.

The world all might be a better place,
Even if technology takes us to space.
Year 2000.

Fashion might change,
And look very strange.
Year 2000.

Will we have TV or radio,
But I hope it doesn't go.
Year 2000.

Will football still be played?
If yes, will the players be paid?
Year 2000.

Will the music be the same?
Will there be any more quiz games?
Year 2000.

This is what it will be in the year 2000,
I wonder what it will be like in year 3000?
Year 2000.

James Wiles (11)
Anthony Roper CP School

CELEBRATION 2000

The millennium is nearly here,
Just sit back and have no fear.
Think of all these inventions,
Give it time and some attention.
The millennium inventions!

People talk about the Millennium Bug,
They ask me and I just shrug.
The computers might just blow,
And leave us with nowhere to go.
The Millennium Bug!

I can't wait till I hear my clock,
Go on twelve with a 'tick tock'.
Think that there may be disasters,
That might need more than a few plasters!
The millennium problems!

Think of all this fashion,
About clothes and passion.
Big Ben getting ready to ding,
Waiting for our presents to bring.
The year 2000 fashions!

Schools may be all technology,
CD may be all Prodigy.
Music could go through changes,
Through all of the ranges.
The millennium technology!

Will there be lots of parties,
Or huge celebrations?
I don't really care,
As long as we all share.
The millennium celebrations

Hadleigh Wiles (11)
Anthony Roper CP School

A New Thousand Years

A brand new thousand years are here,
You should have no fear.
People celebrate,
Will the world vibrate?

No more wars,
Keep the laws.
Lots of friends,
Don't kill hens.

You are boring,
England is scoring.
Don't pollute the Earth,
Instead grow turf.

We hear the birds,
There's lots of herds.
The world is old,
You've been told.

Now we don't break the laws,
We open the doors.
We don't need prisons,
We've got visions.

No more houses,
Without any mouses.
Got a book,
Have a look.

Laura Wilcoxon (9)
Brenzett CE Primary School

THE YEAR I'VE BEEN WAITING FOR

I am waiting for that year to come
It's the millennium, it's just begun
I like it better than last year's party
Food, beer and wine, it's that year
And it's here.

I celebrate, I cannot wait
My friends are late
This is the year I've been waiting for
To celebrate the new millennium.

We have a new year with dancing right here
This is the happiest year
I like it better than all those years.

Samantha Frith (8)
Brenzett CE Primary School

MILLENNIUM

M illennium is great
I mportant news, the millennium is here
L et the millennium be heard about
L isten everybody the millennium is on its way
E verybody celebrates
N ight falls, we can't wait till next year
N ew millennium is nearly here
I can't wait
U se less petrol please
M illennium's here, yippee!

Harriet Gurr (9)
Brenzett CE Primary School

THE NEW MILLENNIUM

The new millennium is here at last,
please let us not repeat the past.
Where wars were fought and people died,
where bombs were dropped, no place to hide.
Where seas turned brown and fishes choked,
where skies turned grey and filled with smoke.
That was the past but now it's the future,
so come on everybody and now get together.

I don't know why we said goodbye,
but I don't know why we had to sigh.

The world is round
and filled with sounds,
with hurt and sadness
and all those things.

So let's be glad that the future's here,
because the New Year has appeared.

Jessica Martin (8)
Brenzett CE Primary School

ANIMALS

When the animals run they eat their food
Please look after cats and other living creatures
Don't let the dogs itch and scratch
Please look after the world better than us
Please drive carefully and look carefully
Please don't let the cats and dogs go on the road
Don't forget what I said, please
Please don't let cats and dogs run out.

David Carnell (9)
Brenzett CE Primary School

A NEW HOPE!

We can all feel the Earth's atmosphere,
so let's be good,
if we all want food,
so don't be silly if you're bustling busy,
let's get:-
rubbish in the bin,
not open tins,
you never know hedgehogs could get in,
cut their necks,
so let's check:-
tins are shut,
or crushed.
We want new health,
not open mouths,
ears that can't hear,
noses that can't smell,
it's like a spell cast over us,
but no fuss,
we can make the world a better place,
so now's the time to shout,
millennium!

Emma Louise Keerie (8)
Brenzett CE Primary School

THE NEW MILLENNIUM FOAL

The new millennium has bought cheers not fears
Everybody open their beers
The foal's mother is happy to get out on the grass
The owner peeps out of the window at the foal
Remember this cold frosty day.

Sarah Richardson (8)
Brenzett CE Primary School

A New Wish

A new hope is in our heads,
for the children that don't have beds,
that they will have all they wish,
to eat from a dish.

Everything that they have,
is only a small wave,
so let's give the people what they need,
It's not just a silly deed.

We can do it if we care,
so let's not despair,
let's help the poor,
it's not against the law.

Jayde Wren (9)
Brenzett CE Primary School

Millennium

Millennium is here at last
We've got a new chance
To stop the wars, pollution and waste as well
We have a new start to get along
With other people and other things
Like in Japan they will have new inventions
We will have digital TV
We could have a new start
If we just start again.

Daniel Clark (8)
Brenzett CE Primary School

I SEE A FISH

I see a fish in the sea
I see the fish is cold
The orange scaly skin
Stands out big and bold.

I see a fish in the sea
I see its fins on the side
The water skims to each side
As his fins gently glide.

I see a fish in the sea
I see the fish diving to the seabed
I think it was a dream
Swimming in my head.

Benjamin Wyatt (9)
Brenzett CE Primary School

I SEE A HORSE

I see a horse in the meadow,
chewing at the green grass.
I see a horse in the meadow,
a motorbike goes past.

I see a horse in the meadow,
galloping at 90 miles per hour.
I see a horse getting sweaty,
I think it needs a shower.

I see a horse in the meadow,
I see it every day,
Until one day when I was driving past,
I found out it had run away.

Peter Pike (10)
Brenzett CE Primary School

I SEE A DOLPHIN

I see a dolphin
jumping up with glee
I wonder what it might see
under the deep dark sea.

I see a great grey dolphin
jumping out the sea
trying to catch some fish
and smiling at me.

I see a dolphin
with his beak wide open
I think it is a great creature
that God has chosen.

Becky Clark (9)
Brenzett CE Primary School

I SEE A SEAGULL

I see a seagull
Squawking in the sand
Now he is surfing in the sky
And diving to the sea.

He swoops up in the air
With a wriggling fish
He sinks back on the sand
As it struggles to be free.

Some other gulls are coming in
But it's too late for them
For he has swallowed his prey.

Alan Morris (9)
Brenzett CE Primary School

I See A Horse

I see a horse trotting in the woods
on its way to the country lane
dogs barking at him as he goes by
but he just trots on past the howling dogs.

I see a horse walking down the quiet country lane
hearing the traffic on a busy road
from so very far away and eating the
wet green grass on the roadside.

I see a horse cantering in the field
jumping over the fences
and treading in the slushy mud
making it go all over his hooves.

I see a horse going back to his stable
his owner giving him a clean up and
giving him a special treat
for being good on the long hack.

Caroline Grimaldi (11)
Brenzett CE Primary School

The Swallow

The swoop of the swallow
swerving in the sun.
The singing of the starling
swishing through the sky.

The swirl of the sauce
simmering in the pan.
The wobble of the jelly
wobbling, ready for us to eat.

The old wise snake
shedding his skin.
The swoop of the monkey
swinging from the branches.

Bethany Dearlove (10)
Brenzett CE Primary School

I SEE A HORSE

I see a horse on the beach
Cantering towards me
I see a horse on the beach
Swimming in the sea.

I see a horse on the beach
Dogs go walking past
Owners watching dogs
As time goes flowing fast.

I see a horse on the beach
Go galloping on by
It's going very, very fast
In front of my eye.

I see a horse on a country lane
Trotting past the main road
He's going so fast
He almost trod on a toad.

I see a horse going back to the stables
Having lunch at one of the tables.

Nicola Watts (11)
Brenzett CE Primary School

I See A Diving Dolphin

I see a diving dolphin
Splashing in the sea,
The bluey-grey colour
Always watching me.

I see a leaping dolphin
Jumping up with song,
The bluey-grey colour
It's so very long.

I see a diving dolphin
Splashing with his tail,
The bluey-grey colour
Attracting a female.

I see a leaping dolphin
Wriggling in fright,
The bluey-grey colour
Looking into the night.

Aspen Wren (9)
Brenzett CE Primary School

Winter

It was a glistening, gleaming, sparkling winter's day
with no one to talk to and nothing to play with
except for a beautiful falling blanket of cold, woolly snow.
From upstairs in my room
I look down from an iced-up window
but I can see nothing but thick, fluffy snow.

Steven Jones (10)
Brenzett CE Primary School

I SEE A BADGER

I see a badger
Running across the road
I see a baby badger
Playing with a toad

I see a badger
Slipping under the hedge
Feeding her tiny babies
Sitting on a ledge

I see a badger
Lying on its head
A car's just run it over
I'm afraid it's very dead.

Benedict Standen (10)
Brenzett CE Primary School

I SEE A HORSE

I see a horse
Waiting to commence,
Runs onto the track,
Up and over the fence.

Gallops around the course,
Canters back to his shed,
Lays onto the straw,
A lovely cosy bed.

Victoria Richardson (11)
Brenzett CE Primary School

I See A Crab

I see a crawling crab,
scrambling at top speed,
taking all the food we eat,
from dinner plates we need.

It's being very naughty,
rushing to and fro,
I'd like to shoot it with a shotgun,
because I hate it so.

But now it's going to the rocks,
(thank my lucky stars,)
I think of it as a horrible demon,
an alien from Mars.

Callum John Mann (9)
Brenzett CE Primary School

I See A Chicken

I see a chicken in the road
Squawking about like a nutter
He pecks on a piece of tarmac
Suddenly he trips on a piece of butter.

I see a chicken in the road
He sees Luke
His stomach turns over
He's just about to puke.

Chantelle Washford (11)
Brenzett CE Primary School

I See A Great White Shark

I see a great white shark
munching salmon fish
Next he's swimming to me
with a plate and dish.

I see a great white shark
coming near to me
I start the motor to get away
it looks like I'm its tea.

I see a great white shark
coming to eat me up
I reach into my pocket
and got some 7-Up.

I see a great white shark
floating to the ground
Thank you 7-Up
for giving him a pound.

Felix Brason (10)
Brenzett CE Primary School

Even

Poor people need a lot
Middle people need some
Famous people need a little
Rich people need nothing
Now we all are even.

Amy Banyon (11)
Chiddingstone CE Primary School

THE MAGIC HOLE

I shall drop in the hole,
The most expensive piece of clothing,
A breath of 500,000 year old air,
A book containing every book.

I shall drop in the hole,
A statue fashioned of gold platinum,
A complete universe,
A 20th century video.

I shall drop in the hole,
A baby's steady breathing rhythm,
A hair of a lion,
A 2nd century skull.

I shall now fill in the hole.

John Cackett (9)
Chiddingstone CE Primary School

I WILL PUT IN MY HEAD

I will put in my head,
the feeling of a baby's soft skin,
the feeling of the warm sun on my face,
a shimmer from the shiniest fish,
the touch of the tiger's fur.

I will put in my head,
the voice of my mum when she's reading me a story,
the sound of the sea lapping on the shore,
the feeling of my eyes shutting as I fall asleep,
the feeling of my dog's tongue as she licks my arm.

Ellie Harris (9)
Chiddingstone CE Primary School

My Secret Box

I will put in my secret box . . .

a silk-like feather from a dodo,
a handful of snow from the Antarctic,
a gold nugget from a gold mine.

I will put in my secret box . . .

a Genie that can grant wishes,
a mysterious and magical golden Phoenix,
a T-rex from Jurassic Park.

I will put in my secret box . . .

luckiness for a generation or two,
confidence for secondary school,
dreams that are totally fantasy.

James Pickard-Eastwood (10)
Chiddingstone CE Primary School

My Photo Album

I will put in my photo album, decorated in gold and silver:
A single shiny scale from the strongest snake,
The taste of icing sugar,
The feel of the hamster's back,
The hotness from the frightening flames in the fire.

I will put in my photo album, decorated in gold and silver:
The smell of a baby's hair after a bath,
A single grain of sand from the beach,
The feel of popping bubble wrap,
And the feel of the waves running through my toes.

Nancy Goldman-Edwards (10)
Chiddingstone CE Primary School

THE THINGS I TREASURE

The things I treasure are,
a tiny golden star,
a baby's rabbit fur,
and the smell of myrrh.

The things I treasure are,
a gold coin from afar,
a green pixie's hat,
a white whisker of a cat.

The things I treasure are,
a colourful sweet jar,
a petal of a flower,
a mighty strong power.

The things I treasure are,
a bite of a chocolate bar,
a single strand of human hair,
a big balloon from the fair.

The things I treasure are,
a tiny golden star,
a baby rabbit's fur,
and the smell of myrrh.

Kalyani McCarthy (10)
Chiddingstone CE Primary School

IN MY BROTHER'S DINNER

In my brother's dinner there would be . . .

the smell of burnt rubber
charcoal from the smuggler's fire
and the tip of a rattlesnake's rattle.

Even more there would be . . .

the stinky smelly smothering breath of a panting dog
the sting of a wasp's tail
and the leftovers from last year's Christmas!

Even more there would be . . .

the soaking shrivelled up smell of last season's dinner
the sticky slimy tail of the stinky slug
and ear wax from someone who hasn't bathed in years!

Ellen Matkins (10)
Chiddingstone CE Primary School

I WILL PUT IN MY PARADISE ROOM

I will put in my paradise room

The smell of a rose
The soul of a protective Chinese dragon
The clouds from heaven

I will put in my paradise room

A pinch of golden dust
A glass of the water from Niagara Falls
Some wool from a golden sheep.

Finlay Robertson (9)
Chiddingstone CE Primary School

IN MY SISTER'S DRINK

In my sister's drink there would be . . .
a flick of a flame
from a bush fire in China,
some flaked mouse skull
from an intelligent mouse
and the biggest tornado
straight from America.

In my sister's drink there would be . . .
a rain cloud to freeze her
shipped from the skies,
the comb from a cockerel
including the bones
and the poisonous breath
of a bi-coloured rock snake.

So I'll heat her up, blow her away
and freeze her down.
How will she look afterwards?

Louise Robinson (9)
Chiddingstone CE Primary School

THE MAGIC BOX

I would like in my box
a crown from King Richard
a palace orange and blue
a bloodstained magic sword

I would like in my box
a shield of confidence
a tip of a whisker of a golden cat
the love of the people who care

I would like in my box
the football of Michael Owen
the gloves of Gordon Banks
Zidane's World Cup winning shirt.

Timothy Corby (10)
Chiddingstone CE Primary School

IN MY WORLD

In my world there are:

Green elephants with red shoes,
Flying fish and furry frogs,
And lots of lots of invisible.

In my world there are:

Mile high skyscrapers,
And lots of hovercrafts,
And merry people having a good old laugh.

In my world there are:

Hardly any schools,
But lots of football,
Haunted houses with ghosts and ghouls.

In my world there are:

Red skies and yellow clouds,
Little babies that aren't loud,
And old people on old sticks.

Now this is my world.

Daniel Weeks (11)
Chiddingstone CE Primary School

A Ride At The Funfair By The Sea

Halfway down the queue,
My stomach lurches,
Is it too late to turn back?
Give the man the money.
On you go.
Strapped in the cart, is it safe?
Will it hold me?
Look up to the pinnacle - off we go!
Climbing, swerving, jolting, stopping,
Starting, racing, screeching.
We're there!
At the pinnacle,
The cold, damp air hits us
And steams our faces.
Our mouths open, gaping
As we plummet down to earth.

William Mayes (10)
Chiddingstone CE Primary School

A Special Box

In my special box I will put:
The tip top of a prize pyramid,
The beach of Barbados
And a lush green jungle.

In my special box I will put:
The flag from the faraway moon,
A shooting, shining, star shooting through the solar system
And a ring of Saturn.

In my special box I will put . . .
A whale spouting out water,
A lion's mane
And a snake's scale.

My box is now crammed full!

Louise Cackett (10)
Chiddingstone CE Primary School

MY MEMORY BOX

I have in my memory box . . .

The first note played on the piano,
The feel of a baby's soft skin,
The smell of a blown-out candle,
The sight of a fading sunset.

I have in my memory box . . .

The last stair in the sky before dawn,
The sound of the waves crashing against rocks,
The heat of a furious fire,
The taste of freshly baked bread.

I have in my memory box . . .

The whole of the Indian Ocean,
The feel of a small smooth pebble,
The sight of a fairy's small transparent wing
And the sound of a dog barking when night has fallen.

Zoë Quirk (11)
Chiddingstone CE Primary School

My Memory

In my memory I will keep:
The first sight of my niece fast asleep,
The holidays I've been on,
The good times I've had with my family.

In my memory I will keep:
All of my birthdays when I was young,
The Christmas parties with friends
And other times like that.

In my memory I will keep:
The fact I'm alive and well,
My family who brought me up
And the first sight of my dog
As a puppy running along the road.

There will soon be some more I hope.

Andrew Lucas (10)
Chiddingstone CE Primary School

My Tea

I'm going to have in my tea for starters,
The finest fish from the bottom of the ocean,
The best juice from the best orange.

I'm going to have in my tea for the main course,
Freshly sliced and grilled chicken and vegetables
picked from the heaven's garden,
Gravy from dinosaur stock and potatoes
from the middle of the earth.

Nicholas Hards (10)
Chiddingstone CE Primary School

HARLEQUINS

I'm on my way to see the match
Wearing my badge of gold.
A hat of burgundy on my head
And a scarf that's really old.
The adrenaline's flowing,
My heart is going
. . . to explode.

Through the ticket barrier we go,
Hot dogs in our hand.
We wander down the corridor
Until we reach our stand.
The adrenaline's flowing,
My heart is going
. . . to explode.

The players run out, the match begins,
Will Carling scores a try.
But Wasps come back and score a goal,
I think I'm going to die.
The adrenaline's flowing,
My heart is going
. . . to explode.

'Yippee!' screamed the crowd as they jumped
up and down,
'We're through to the finals at last!
We're on our way to win the crown.'
My heart really *is* beating fast!

Becky Stanley, Megan Roberts, Daley Bibby, Victoria Castle,
Nicola Ward, Laura Allen, Sian English & Michelle Jermin
Days Lane Primary School

The Little Snowman

The sky is cold and grey
Winter is on its way
Little snowflakes gently fall
Start to cover the garden wall.

Children look out to see
The snowflakes falling on the tree
Children put on coats and scarves
Build a snowman on the grass.

Two eyes, a scarf, a pipe and a hat
So white, so tall, not thin but fat
The sun is shining really bright
Which melt away the snowflakes white.

Hollie Lawrence & Chanelle Handley (9)
Days Lane Primary School

The Ice Princess

She glides across the countryside
Her cloak opens out very wide
Frosty fingers touch the night sky
Her only light, the stars so high
She walks across the river bank
Water turns into silver ice
Spring is coming, she dies away.

Sarah Henry (10) & Sara Kenney (9)
Days Lane Primary School

MY BRACE

Your teeth are all nooky and cranny,
worse than your great, great granny.
My orthodontist smiled with glee,
another little boy who can't eat steak for tea.

When the brace was fitted
I couldn't speak at all,
all the other children laughed at me
and said I was a fool.

Things are getting better,
my teeth are really straight
and all the girls at my school
think I'm really great.

Alex Pankhurst (10)
Days Lane Primary School

IT'S SNOWING

Snow is falling on the trees and the bush
Tomorrow, I fear brings more snow
It's snowing but I like it
It's cold but I don't care.

It goes along like a mysterious painter
Colouring the garden all white
Cars and fields all turn white
At the hands of this mysterious man.

The leaves drop like a football bouncing.
Leaves on the ground wither away
No leaves tomorrow, I fear
But that's because it's snowing!

Daniel Haley (10)
Days Lane Primary School

A Walk In The Woods

Every day I go down to the woods,
    I hear talking,
    Rustling of leaves,
    Rattle of the fence,
    Singing of the birds high up in the trees.
I then stomp, stomp, stomp on the hard mud,
    I crunch the leaves on the floor,
    I snap branches off the trees.
Then, before I go home,
I squelch and squish in the mud.
    I stop for a minute,
    I hear a faint voice,
    It's coming from my house.
I know who it is,
It's my grandma Joyce.
She wants me to have some sizzling sausage
with crunchy chips
and lemonade that fizzes in my mouth.

Sophie Durham (9)
Days Lane Primary School

Dirty Dad

My dad is really dirty
He smells like cheesy feet
He never wears a shirt for tea
Not a person you want to meet

His hair is very curly
He never shaves his beard
His face is covered in spots
And he is certainly very weird

He eats a lot of fatty food
He's always on the booze
He's really dumb at DIY
And comes home for a snooze

He picks his nose and dirty toes
And even scratches his bum
He keeps his money in the loo
And this shows he's very dumb.

Mitchell Murrell & Graham Hawley (10)
Days Lane Primary School

AT THE SEASIDE

> Clapping, tapping,
> Laughing, screaming,
> Whistling, shouting and
> Thumping.

> > That's what the
> > Children do.

Well, the adults are
Very boring. All
They do
Is talk.
The sea thumping
Up the rocks,
The seagulls crying.

> > Some children splashing,
> > Some even throw
> > The ball in the air and it lands
> > With a big *splat!*

Luke Fenn (10)
Days Lane Primary School

River

Rapid waver
Calm wrinkler
Canoe dasher
Boat racer
Fish wisher
Face exciter
Person amuser
Down streamer.

Katherine Ritchie (10)
East Stour CP School

The Clouds

Moving with the wind
Travelling all round the world
Trying to be friends
The aeroplanes fly straight through
Making pictures like a face.

Stuart Conochie (11)
East Stour CP School

Thunder

Rumbling,
It collides with wreckage.
Illuminated electric,
Booming.

David Phillips (10)
East Stour CP School

IF I COULD...

If I could draw the life of a bee,
I would draw a wonder of the world.
If I could draw further in time,
I would draw the sweeping stars.
If I could taste the crying of a girl down the street,
I would sense the heart of someone who felt alien.
If I could feel the lungs of a bear,
I would touch the voice of a singer.

Kirsty Olson (9)
East Stour CP School

HAILSTORM

Hailstorm
Pitting down as
It taps on the door
It chuckles harmoniously
With a loud snort.

Emma Turner (9)
East Stour CP School

CHICKEN LEGS

Cook them in the pot
Serve them on your plate, eat them,
Then run to the loo.

Kaylie Russell (9)
East Stour CP School

GREAT GREAT GRANDAD

I've been told you were 24,
when you went away and died in the war.
There are lots of things I'd like to ask,
if only I could go back in the past.

How old were you,
Did you have friends?
Who were they,
Did you write letters to send?

I know you were in France,
in Flanders' field,
were there any poppies in it,
when you were killed?

Did you live in a trench,
with bags full of sand?
Did you have to crawl,
over no-man's land?

Did you fight,
did you have a gun?
Did you walk,
or did you run?

Was it dark and cold,
were you scared?
I think you were brave,
I wouldn't have dared.

I want you to know,
we all remember,
by buying a poppy,
on the 11th of November.

Abigail Ireland (10)
East Stour CP School

I Would...

I would like to taste the sweetness of the flower in the summer,
The delicious food in another faraway universe,
The blue of the sky
And the green of the grass.

I wish I could touch the song of a baby bird in spring,
The twinkling stars at night,
The soul of a caring person
And the golden rays of light
from the sparkling sun on a warm summer's morning.

I should be miles tall and see into space,
I should be a lion and chase tiny meerkats,
I should be a person in the future
And I should be a beautiful bird and warble
a lovely heart-warming tune.

I would like to see the howl of the amazing wolf
on a summer's evening,
The cry of an injured baby fox cub,
The dinosaurs from the faraway past
And my Stone Age ancestors' memories.

Karina Sturch (10)
East Stour CP School

My Cat

Fur licker
Guest percher
Lap wriggler
Face scratcher
My cat Sweep.

Gemma Lincoln (11)
East Stour CP School

Miaow Went The Parrot

Miaow went the parrot,
Woof went the hamster,
Squawk went the kitten,
Ssss went the gerbils,
Squeak went the dog.

Hee-haw, hee-haw
Was that you Mum?
You are funny!

Louise Weeden (8)
East Stour CP School

Tracey Beaker

Impetigo face,
Malevolent eyes,
Miniature lips,
Cool mum,
Difficult hair,
Black.

Lauren Mackelborough (10)
East Stour CP School

Thunder

Clash and
Crash as I swoop,
Through the sky with lightning
At my side, lighting up the sky
Tonight.

Jenni Steele (11)
East Stour CP School

2000

What is happening,
What's going on?
Aliens have been sighted,
Everybody's excited,
Lots of things to do!

What's going on?
All the sadness has gone.
We are looking forward to the year
2000!

Katherine Pitt (10)
East Stour CP School

MOON

I glow,
With a soft beam,
I shine through the window,
I dance in a sky of bright stars,
Shimmer.

Kate Collingridge (11)
East Stour CP School

EGGS

Spitting in the pan,
gazing up like gleaming eyes,
taste yummy on toast.

Karly Medcalf (11)
East Stour CP School

THE MILLENNIUM

The millennium's here,
I'm not quite sure if I should be excited or worried.

A creature's coming to invade the computers.
I'm not quite sure if I should be excited or worried.

Will it climb through the drainpipes or knock politely at the door
And say . . .
       'I'm coming to invade your computer.'

I'm not quite sure if I should be excited or worried.

No, no of course not!
It will creep to us overnight
While we are asleep.

*I'm warning you
Be scared!*

Kaylie Cairns (10)
Egerton CE Primary School

MILLENNIUM

M agical moments at the millennium,
I ngenious idea, the wonderful Dome.
L essons learnt from the past,
L aughing people everywhere.
E xcited people everywhere,
N oise of happy children.
N attering parents having fun,
I lluminated streets.
U proar as the excitement builds,
M illennium is here.

Scarlett Atkins (9)
Egerton CE Primary School

THE MILLENNIUM - WHAT'S HAPPENING NEXT?

Through the next thousand years you'd better beware
Or at the end you'll be in despair!

We all expect on New Year's Eve
The Millennium Bug our computer to seize
But it will eat the human race
It won't leave of us a single trace.

That's what's happening next!

We don't think that Martians are real
But in a year's time before them we'll kneel
In the year two thousand we'll taste defeat
Just two days after we meet.

That's what's happening next!

We all think that we're safe on the Earth
It's where our mothers had our birth
But the gods have decided to select
The Earth as the next victim for the greenhouse effect.

That's what's happening next!

In the year two thousand a rock from space
A meteorite will smash the Earth's face
All life on Earth will die in an hour
The animals on Earth will have no power.

That's what's happening next!

James Alexander Cox (10)
Egerton CE Primary School

MILLENNIUM POEM

M illennium Dome's completion is near
I t's very big but nothing to fear
L ondon is where it's going to be
L ots of people looking to see
E verybody is delighted
N obody's getting over excited
N ote that it's going to be cool
I t's a shame it hasn't got a swimming pool
U nder a big roof
M ost likely to be waterproof.

Cameron Forbes (10)
Egerton CE Primary School

MILLENNIUM

M illennium is nearly here
I nteresting things
L ots of people getting ready for the year 2000
L aughing people ready to come
E veryone is excited they can't wait
N oisy people in the pub
N ot a lot of work is done
I f all the work is done we can have some fun
U sually we have some fun
M illennium is here for the year.

Katrina Saunders (10)
Egerton CE Primary School

CELEBRATION

C elebrate the new year
E lderly people enjoying the new year
L uxury Lambhorginis going fast
E nding the year '99
B abies being born
R ailways being built
A ctors acting out new movies
T opping up drinks for when the clock strikes twelve
I gnoring intelligent actors
O ctopuses appear in the sea
N ext year is the year 2000.

Arnold Duncan (9)
Egerton CE Primary School

MILLENNIUM POEM

M illennium Dome coming soon
I t's a new year and we celebrate the Dome
L ooking good and lovely
L icking lovely lollies
E verybody getting scared as aliens are getting closer
N o one is there
N othing is left in their houses
I nteresting things are getting built, like computers
U sually the computers are getting broke by a Millennium Bug, the
M illennium will soon be here.

Christopher Holmes (10)
Egerton CE Primary School

MILLENNIUM DOME

Many people will come to see the
Millennium Dome.

Interesting it will be, with thousands of people.

Crowds of people coming to admire it.

It's coming soon, the big Bug's coming,
I'm not quite sure when *but it's coming.*

Millennium, millennium, I can't wait till the millennium.

It's just struck twelve o'clock oh no!
It's here!

Alexa Jay Craven (10)
Egerton CE Primary School

THE MILLENNIUM POEM

M en building the Millennium Dome
I t's getting higher
L ights are going up
L ifts get fitted
E very day a little bit more is done
N ews reporters everywhere
N early done, nearly done
I t's on the news
U sually at tea
M illennium Dome, will it be finished in time?

Holly Atkins (11)
Egerton CE Primary School

THE MILLENNIUM BUG

Dong!
Dong!
The clock strikes twelve.
Dong!
Dong!
The world howls!
The Millennium Bug is really here,
I can definitely hear it sneer,
Hey! Who switched off the light,
Now I'm left in the dead of night.

Dates are whizzing round my room,
Am I now in the grip of doom?
Now what's that blue thing in the air,
I feel I want to stop and stare.

The thing said 'Sorry to drive you round the bend,
But I'm afraid the world's about to end.'
Dong!
Dong!

With a clash, a bang and a flash of light,
The bug and the world flew out of sight.
I had to clench my mattress tight,
Because this gave me an awful fright.

Then with a great glitter and gleam,
I found that it was all a dream!

Dong!

Kit Rowe (9)
Egerton CE Primary School

Millennium

The millennium is the turning of time
As it goes round the world and still the world lives on!
Let's party!
Let's party!
For 2000 years humans have been born and died
We'll celebrate this day and, in my bed I'll lay knowing
that people all over the world will be celebrating this special day.
The Millennium Dome should be finished in time
The Millennium Bug committing a heinous crime
Everything is going on, on 1st January 2000.

Charlotte Button (10)
Egerton CE Primary School

The Millennium Dome

Millennium magic all the way,
£1.50 that's all you've got to pay,
When people see the Millennium Dome,
You will see when they go home,
They will say,
That was a super day,
But when it comes to an end,
It drives people round the bend,
But when people say goodnight,
They all snuggle up tight.

Charlotte Manning (9)
Egerton CE Primary School

MILLENNIUM BUG

Most vicious bug,
Ignores the top signs,
Listening to all man's plans,
Leaves no trail,
Except a broken plug.
Never seen, nothing left,
Inside your wires,
Undoing all your games,
making havoc on the net.

Bug alert!
Ultra bug alert!
Get out quick!

Ben Madden (10)
Egerton CE Primary School

THE MILLENNIUM

Millennium's arrived,
It's midnight,
Lots of people party,
Lots of shouts and cheers,
Even children shout and dance,
Nationally adults drink to the millennium,
Nationally people cheering down the road,
It's time to party,
Up and cheer,
Millennium's here!

Harriet Adams (9)
Egerton CE Primary School

THE MILLENNIUM

M illennium will be here in a year's time
I n the year 2000
L ots of people will be celebrating
L oving the parties they might go to
E veryone knows it will be New Year
N ew models will be in the Millennium Dome
N icely displayed for people to see
I n people will go
U ntil they've had their fun
M ost will like it except for maybe some.

Charlotte Dray (10)
Egerton CE Primary School

THE MILLENNIUM DOME

M ost people will be really excited
I n the year 2000
L ovely new things
L ots of children like the shape of the new Dome
E lderly people don't know what's going on
N o interest in it do Kim and Laura Jayne have
N ew toys are being made
I s it going to be finished in time?
U nusual place to go
M any people want to go there, do Kim and Laura? No!

Laura Filmer (11)
Egerton CE Primary School

NIGHT

The night was innocent, cold and damp
With gleaming golden eyes
Coming through the thick black stillness.
In the distance I hear screeches loud and clear
The bats are shuddering endlessly, the shadows of them are upon the ground.
Oh no! The evil faces have come again
I'd much rather be in my bed alone.
The gate squeaks,
I hear quickening footsteps on the crispy, frost-laden leaves.
Aaah!
The thing is, was it only a dream?

Oliver Hill (10)
Friars School

THE SEA IS MUCH BIGGER THAN A PEA

The sea is much bigger than a pea,
But smaller than the sky.
Its waves mountain high,
It blows on your face in disgrace,
Angry waves have no steady pace,
The rocks have been cracked,
By the loud smack of the blue sea,
But the sea is still much bigger than a pea.

I am sad because the sea is being bad,
The sea's only fault is it smells of salt.
It looks rough and very tough,
But the sea is still bigger than a pea.

David Leavey (10)
Friars School

THE THING

The 'Thing' lies under the sink,
The 'Thing' is something I think.
Does he exist or is he fiction?
Where does he live, attic or kitchen?

He crawls about
In and out.

He is covered in mould,
Many days old.
He loves to haunt me
Always to follow me.

He crawls about,
In and out.

Why is he pink?
Why does he stink?
What does he eat?
Vegetables or meat?

The beast must be intelligent,
He has managed to drive me bent.
Every day he is there,
On the window sill, on the stair.
Nobody can see him but me,
Should I stay, scream or flee?

Nikhil Sanyal (11)
Friars School

Storm

Thunder crashing loudly in the sky
Wind battering against your bedroom window
Trees swaying and bending like elastic bands
Twisted branches
Twigs crashing against the window,
Rain pounding against the glass.
Leaves being tossed in the wind
Trees disintegrating into sticks.
Wind whistling,
Trees bending like crooked old men
And hail crashing to the ground.

Lee Barrett
Friars School

Storm

Half asleep in my bed;
Wind blowing the leaves off the trees.
The trees getting blown to sticks
Twigs tapping violently on the window;
The wind whistling through the trees.
Trees bending like elastic bands
Rain pounding against the window like waves crashing the rocks.
Leaves being tossed in the wind;
Trees trembling in the fierce storm.

Joe Ottaway (9)
Friars School

STORM

A storm is an event when the trees are
trembling
And the trees are rustling like the sea on
pebbles.
I was asleep when this happened.
I woke with a start and saw a flash of
lightning pierce the darkness.
Will it stop? I wonder.
The twigs were knocking on the door
The rain was racing down the window . . .
I don't like storms.

Stefan Pfefferlé (10)
Friars School

NIGHT

Spine-chilling sounds
Coming from the church
Gleaming golden eyes from within the thick, black stillness.
Mysterious shadows looming
Coming from the silent night
With twisted branches making gloomy shadows,
Squeaking gates and eerie sounds
Come creeping through the rustling trees
Each night in the graveyard,
Then silently creep away
Into the dark.

Nicholas Schatunowski (10)
Friars School

NIGHT

The darkness of the night,
With spine-chilling noises,
Gleaming golden eyes and shadows looming,
Once innocent trees now have evil faces,
Hunchback shapes that creep and crowd,
Twisted branches and loud screeches,
Squeaking gates,
Moonlit gardens,
Creatures hiding,
Morning approaching,
Eerie noises,
Quickening footsteps,
Trees laughing,
Thick black, no light,
Morning's brightness rising.

Mark Ashley (10)
Friars School

THE CAT

Milly, Milly slim and sleek
Ready for danger
Silent while she watches her prey
Looks cautiously around
Gracefully tiptoes
Leaving twenty little footprints.
Pricks up her ears at the tiniest noise
Jumps higher than a rabbit
Never makes a sound.

William Fletcher (10)
Friars School

THE SEA

Waves crashing on rocks like a
baseball bat.
Wind blowing off the sailor's hat.
Rain beating against you.
Waves turning from black to blue.
Waves so aggravated they crash against
the wall.
The wind howls while the seagulls fall.
Waves pull ships down by using
invisible hands.
Wind sending froth on the dark dull sands.

To the people's alarm,
The sea has suddenly become calm.
Sun comes out and stops the rain.
The rocks are slowly overcoming the pain.
Sea is becoming clear
And the gulls are coming near.
The shipwrecked sailors slowly appear.

James Loudon (10)
Friars School

NIGHT

The eerie noises make the night more frightening,
The scurrying, snuffling creatures,
With their golden, gleaming eyes.
The squeaking gates and the quickening footsteps,
Make the thick, black darkness of the night even longer.

The hunchback shapes that creep and crowd,
The spine-chilling sounds from the evil . . . something.
The twisted branches make the shadows more dooming,
The morning sun rises,
Finally I can rest.

Rosie Ransley (10)
Friars School

NIGHT

The night-time is all so calm,
Just the trickle of the stream.
The moonlight shining on the fields,
Which makes them all shine.

But still there is a scary side,
Where owls and bats flap about.
The trees and plants make scary shapes,
Which make you jump in fright.

The moon lights the gardens up,
So pretty and so nice.
If you look up at the stars at night,
They look so beautifully bright.

Soon it is the end of night,
So the animals go back inside.
But day goes very quickly,
So it is night all over again.

Rebecca Startin (11)
Friars School

NIGHT

Night commences,
like a ghost train,
with creatures ready to jump.

Night,
like a distorted radio,
spine-chilling sounds and eerie noises.

Night,
like shadow puppets,
with hunchback shapes that creep and crowd,
and all the dark things looming.

Night,
with nocturnal creatures,
bats shuddering restlessly,
and innocent trees becoming treacherous beings.

Night,
I don't think it is just thick, black stillness.

Tom Elias (10)
Friars School

NIGHT

The moonlight garden,
With ghostly screams,
Squeaking gates and thick black stillness,
Eerie noises screeching in my ears.

Quickening footsteps past my house,
I'm all tucked up in my bed,
The trees swinging, making faces,
All is quiet and scary.

Golden eyes looking through the trees,
Spine-chilling shapes in the distance,
Soft screeches nearby,
Maybe bats or maybe something else . . .

Alex Smith (10)
Friars School

NIGHT-TIME

The darkness consuming all light from the day,
Once innocent trees, now cast hideous forms,
He quickens his footsteps,
For the moonlight forms treacherous shadows on the path.

Twisting and twirling, the branches in the black,
Shadows looming,
Leaves rustling,
Split second screeches frightening him to death!

Then seldom silently, bats fly through the night!
Golden, yellow eyes shine from the trees,
Mysterious shapes gloom in the moonlight,
Bats shudder, restlessly throughout the night.

Throughout the night the moon shines,
Casting the shadows of the tall dark trees.
Night-time,
Night-time!

Tristan Spencer (10)
Friars School

Night

Suddenly, dark falls consuming all the light,
Quickening footsteps in the distance,
Seldom but silently, bats fly through the night!
Eerie noises disrupt the peaceful evening,
Hunchback shapes that creep and crowd,
Squeaking gates from a person coming home,
Suddenly innocent trees now become treacherous beings,
It is getting towards midnight, thick, black, stillness,
Spine-chilling sounds with gleaming, golden eyes in the distance,
Suddenly there's silence,
An owl hoots in some twisted branches,
Silence! Except for some soft screeches and the river running by,
Silence commences once again.

Christopher Plowman (10)
Friars School

A Stormy Sea

Hissing,
Frothing,
The foam spat like a swirling mass of snakes,
The cry of gulls like banshees,
The lighthouse's timbers creaked like rusty joints,
As the sea raged like an argument
Until,
The first light of dawn crushed the stormy waves.

Benedict Bunyard (10)
Friars School

NIGHT

The night falls in around my head,
Creatures scurrying and snuffling around,
The thick black stillness all around me,
A squeaking gate moving in the wind.
Once an innocent tree now . . .
Casts gloomy shadows upon the ground,
Shadows looming behind the trees,
Ghastly sounds from the trees above.
The moon makes the whole thing an eerie
place to be.
Twisted branches look like faces high up
in the trees.
I am glad when morning comes.

Adam Bushell (10)
Friars School

NIGHT

Do you dare go out at night?
Shadows looming in the dark,
Quickly get back to your home,
Before the devil shows his face,
How evil can night be?

Do you dare go out at night?
The summer's sun once innocent,
Turns into the hunchback moon,
Twisted branches here and there,
Give even the bravest a scare!
RIP.

Joseph Price (9)
Friars School

Past, Present, Future

The past is mainly blurred
but when we arrived at first,
we were in what is known
now as the Stone Age.

As years went, we grew wiser
from stone tools to fire,
and the discovery of metals
we slowly became more
and more advanced.

Until we had televisions
cars and aeroplanes,
which now takes this
poem . . . into the present.

The present is the
one thing that is never
blurred and the one
thing that will never stop.

But the present could
already have happened in
the future and it might
be happening again and
again in the past.

Like a person rewinding
and fast-forwarding
a video tape.
Now I go to the future
but I cannot say anything
about it.

If you want to find out what
it holds for us,
you will have to wait and see
for yourself!

Edward Edmondson (11)
Friars School

THE STORMY NIGHT

Walking down the sandy beach,
The sea crystal clear,
Waves crashing against the rocks,
Seagulls floating in the sky,
The sky a darkish blue,
The wind howling like a wolf,
The sea roaring like a monster,
The smell fresh,
The sea chewing at the smooth round rocks,
Covered in seaweed,
The sea as
Cold as ice,
With waves like hands
To pull you under.
Time has passed
The storm has died.

Emma Cragg (9)
Friars School

NIGHT

Shadows looming in the darkness,
Eerie noises as the night passes by,
Spine-chilling sounds throughout the night.

Hunchbacked creatures looming in the darkness,
Thick, black stillness in the graveyard,
Once innocent trees . . .
Now have evil faces,

Squeaky gates blowing in the wind,
Soft screeches pierce the night,
Bats shuddering in the shadows,

Footsteps quickening as the night goes on,
Moon casting ugly faces on the path,
Trees creaking in the wind.

Damien Bailey (10)
Friars School

THE SHIP AT SEA

I'm in the bottom of the ship,
The pitter patter of raindrops like rocks on a big drum,
The ship's rocking from side to side,
On deck I see waves big as the ship,
Trying to pull us down,
The rugged rocks showing through the sea,
I could hear the crashing of waves on the reef,
The clouds were black and low,
My ship was slowly losing the battle
The froth like whipped cream floating on the rough sea,
The bolts of lightning were like strikes
Of blue paint against the black night sky.

Sebastian Goodwin-Day (10)
Friars School

THE SEA

At night seas are calm
and waters
still
restful
peaceful
and crystal clear
then waters
start to ripple
and vibrate
a storm
breaks out
and seaweed becomes
a writhing monster
below the waves.
Waters crash against
sharp rocks like pins
the waves stumble like
a blind person into
the sandy beach
there's a boat out fishing
its boards creaking.
Smash the
flooding waves
are crashing into
the sinking ship
the fish are gasping
for air
then calmness again
the waters
motionless
peaceful and
still.

Sarah Haselup (10)
Friars School

WINTER WONDERLAND

As the whispering wind softly falls through the polar white treetops,

Snow falls like an owl on its nightly hunts.

Icicles hang like jagged teeth from the window sills of houses.

Mirror ice reflects anything that comes its way.

People's breath resembles the steam of a steam train.

Naked skeletal trees stand with snow-bandaged fingers.

The sky is so dull yet the floor is so bright.

The children's teeth chatter on their way to school.

Hannah Hogben & Becky Bell (7)
Great Chart School

THE WITCH

Torn, tatty rags worn by a ragged witch.

Evil bony claws casting bewitching spells.

Cruel swirling spiteful eyes set in a
Scarred face.

Hair clinging like slimy worms around her
Mouldy crumpled brow.

Her cackling evil shrill laugh echoes in the
Night sky.

Lance Johnson (8)
Great Chart School

THE WITCH

The cursed evil claws rip through her victim's flesh,
She hypnotises people then pierces their bodies,
She liquidises her prey then enchants them,
The witch's eyes swirl and twirl,
She mesmerises animals then turns them into beasts,
She violently kills, then shreds their bodies to bits,
The hag shrieks at midnight when the moon is lit,
She looks at people and the people faint in fright,
She turns to face her victims then in two seconds flat they're in her tummy,
The sorceress heats her cauldron then casts her spells.

Adam Wilkinson (9)
Great Chart School

THE IRON MAN

Pitch-black headlamp eyes glow,
His dustbin-shaped head squeaks as it turns,
Its gigantic iron body is covered with rust,
Tall as the Empire State Building,
He moves his crab-shaped hands towards giant scraps of metal,
He gobbles damaged motor cars.

Rhiannon Simmons & Abigail Ennis (7)
Great Chart School

SNOW

It's like cotton wool on a frosty floor.

It's like a blanket covering the frozen grass in the garden.

It's like a beautiful swan landing and taking off leaving a pile of soft gleaming feathers.

It's like talcum powder on someone's feet.

It's like sugar icing on a Christmas cake at the dinner table.

It's like a glistening jewel on someone's finger.

It's like a big white floss of candy at the fair.

Richard Lyne (10)
Great Chart School

THE WORLD OF WINTER

Shimmering air as sharp as glass.
Mirror-like ice reveals ghostly reflections.
Downy blankets cover the frosted ground.
Ink-black clouds blotch the dull sky.
Skeletal trees rattle in the whistling wind.
Dragon-like people gasp with steam twisting out of their jaws.

Hazel Crisp & Jennifer Keen (8)
Great Chart School

HUMAN WORLD

The fire is in contest against the killing wind.

Stretched spider legs on shivering trees.

People wrapped in thick layers of silk and wool.

Wind whistling with all its might to make the houses tremble.

Misty clouds fluffed up in huge balls.

People's sooty breath is being blurted out.

Nails have been sculpted into daggers and stuck together by the freezing water.

The snow god has commanded snow on the whole world.

The snow world is filled with frozen people with chattering teeth.

The human world is made out of fire and steam as grey as elephant skin.

Thomas Bushnell & Ben Moffat (8)
Great Chart School

THE IRON MAN

His large head appears above the ground
Huge headlamp eyes shine on the anxious farmers
His giant crab-claw hands reach out for scraps of metal

Taller than a huge skyscraper
Even his head is like a rusty dustbin
He reaches out for metal machinery
And crunches it between teeth.

James Barden & Matthew Mansfield (8)
Great Chart School

MY BROTHER DAMON

My brother Damon is only three
he's four and a half years younger than me.

He arrived in summer, it was June I think
he was a lovely baby, all chubby and pink.

He has nut brown hair and blue eyes like Mum
and now he's older we have a lot of fun.

He's mad on dinosaurs which is all very well
but in the mornings he's a T-rex with a roar and a yell.

Sometimes we argue and sometimes we fight about things
                                        that really don't matter
but one thing's for sure whatever he does I love my little brother.

Sam Yates (8)
Great Chart School

YOU ARE LIKE...

You are like cotton wool drifting
across the land

You are like freezing carpet lying on the ground

You are like white feathers
flittering across the world

You are like talcum powder that
children have sprinkled

You are like sugar flattened in a sugar bowl

You are like a wet blanket on the garden.

Cara Jane Shearing (10)
Great Chart School

THE IRON MAN

The iron man sways in the flowing wind,
Then swiftly he topples over.
He lays at the bottom of the cliff,
Broken into pieces.
His hands start scuttling like shiny crabs
They go searching for his arms, torso, legs and head.

Robert Iles (7)
Great Chart School

THE TAPE MEASURE

Liquorice twists polished with azure.
Coiled sapphire vines
Pick it up, see it trapeze.
Crushed tail of a magical aquamarine monkey.
An indigo eel swirling in navy waters.
A bluebell snake slithering through uncut jade grass.

Abby Jones (9)
Great Chart School

THE IRON MAN

An immense black figure stands on the cliff.
His searchlight eyes scan the horizon.
His huge feet shake the ground like a monstrous earthquake.
Made of steel his giant torso gleams in the moonlight
and rattles like a rattlesnake playing a tune.
His dustbin-shaped head swivels on his sturdy neck.

Jennifer Keen, Hazel Crisp & Emily Ford (8)
Great Chart School

CHRISTMAS

The presents delicately wrapped as the children slumber.
Carefully placed under the Christmas tree
waiting to be torn open on Christmas morn.
The baby Jesus Christ swaddled in
warm cloth lies in the manger.
Mary and Joseph overjoyed that
their son is to be king.
The hot Christmas pudding helpless
on a china plate covered in cold cream.
The Christmas turkey lying on a
carving board all stuffed and ready to eat.
The choir gather around doors,
their wonderful singing echoes
through the empty street.
The holly wreaths on the
door shiver as the choir sing merrily.

Kirstie Leigh Atkins (9)
Great Chart School

THE STUBBORN IRON MAN

His eyes, like glowing searchlights in the twilight,
scan the open sea,
His head, shaped as a gleaming dustbin slowly swivels
towards the metallic sounds.

The earth shakes as he tramples over the ground.
His enormous torso rattles like a maraca.
His legs, like long tree trunks
carry his huge body lifting its prey.
His jagged jaws bite into the farmer's machinery.

Hollie Weatherill & Katie Parish (8)
Great Chart School

Rain!

Transparent
  gushing
    rain
      deep
        driving
          drains

Puddles
  filling
    up
      down
        pours
          rain

Deep
  dark
    puddles
      cascading
        rain.

Jason Stewart (9)
Great Chart School

The Iron Man

His large gleaming eyes glowing like stars.
His enormous torso is as large as the earth.
His gigantic legs are as deep as the Atlantic ocean.
His fingers crawl like crabs.
His heart pounds like a bass drum.
His blood leaks like oil.
His feet are as long as four single beds.
His iron is as thick as a tractor's wheel.

Samantha Bacon (8)
Great Chart School

Winter

The fractured ice on the freezing pond.
Naked trees wave in the whistling wind.
Icicles look like silver thorns.
The icy snow under hard, warm shoes,
Children's bright blue lips shine in the frosty air.

Emily Ford (8)
Great Chart School

The Iron Man

Grander than a mansion
He stands higher than a block of flats
Robust legs hold up his immense silvery torso
Eyes like twilight stars scan the horizon
In the moonlight his shadow can be seen over gushing waters.

Becky Bell & Felicity Pentland (7)
Great Chart School

The Iron Man

Pitch-black headlamp eyes glow,
His dustbin-shaped head squeaks as it turns,
His gigantic iron body is covered with rust,
Tall as the Empire State Building,
He moves crab-shaped hands towards giant scraps of metal.

Abigail Ennis (8)
Great Chart School

THE IRON MAN

His headlamp eyes shine out over the farm land
His head, large as a bedroom, turns at the sound of cars
His tree legs come to a standstill
He eats kettles and lorries,
Tractors and barbed wire
He tumbles down the hill
Crashing and bumping
Shaking and creaking
His hand pokes out of the ground
Making mini earthquakes.

Lisette Priestley (8)
Great Chart School

CONVERSATION

Why are your curtains open of a night-time?
I haven't got a clue.

Why are you making Tace a sandwich?
I haven't got a clue.
Why is your bedroom in a mess?
Why did you put gravy in the garden?
I haven't got a clue.
Why do you pick on your brother?
I haven't got a clue.
Why do you keep saying I haven't got a clue?
What do you mean?

Gary Jackson (10)
Harcourt Primary School

UNTITLED

Round and round, twisting, turning, flowing, bending like a tornado.
Whirlpool or a snail shell.
Swirling, whirling, turning.
Always rotating, curling, coiling inwards and outwards
Spinning all around as if it's dancing.
Is it a disk? Is it a loop? Or is it a ring?
It's a winding, curling spiral.
Round and round and round and round and round and round.

Neil Andrews (10)
Harcourt Primary School

UNTITLED

Round and round, spirals twirl like a drill going in to a wall,
Going out of control.
Twisting and turning when you're in your bed
Waiting for the tornado to go and to go and to go.

Alistair Buchanan (11)
Harcourt Primary School

UNTITLED

A spiral spinning around like a mini tornado circling.
It never ends you can stare for ages
Watching it twirling
Around and around and around.

Nicholas Phillipps (11)
Harcourt Primary School

Untitled

Hypnotic spiral.
Twisting circles.
Circulating round.
Dizzy spiral.
Whirling circles.
Slinky on the ground.
Non-stop.
On and on an on and on and on and on and stop.

Sarah Browne (11)
Harcourt Primary School

Untitled

A spiral spins round and round,
Twisting and coiling like a staircase in a castle.
Like a tornado, a whirlpool and a corkscrew.
They will surely make you sick, dizzy as well.

Joshua Graves (11)
Harcourt Primary School

Untitled

Round and round, twist and twirl, I'm in a daze.
I'm spinning clockwise, out of control.
Curling, whirling helter-skelter down and down out of control.
Bending, mending, the spiral patterns bending out of control.

Terri Rees (10)
Harcourt Primary School

WHAT?

Do you want a drink?
What?
Do you want a drink?
What?
Do . . .you . . . want . . . a . . . drink?
What?
Oh I give up!
What?
I wasn't talking to you!
What?
I . . . wasn't . . . talking . . . to . . . you!
What?
Oh just shut up!
What?
Do you want £5?
What? . . . Oh yeah!

Claire Orchard (10)
Harcourt Primary School

MY DEAF NAN

Do you want a piece of toast?
Do I want a piece of post?
I said do you want a piece of toast?
No I don't want a piece of post, it's probably a phone bill.
Shall I make some teas?
No, I don't like peas.
I said teas.
No peas.
Oh I give up.

Chelsey Atkins (9)
Harcourt Primary School

I Don't Know

'Why is your name what it is?'
'I don't know.'
'Why are you dirty?'
'I don't know.'
'Why is your hair sticking up?'
'I don't know.'
'What did you have for breakfast?'
'I don't know.'
'What is your favourite football team?'
'I don't know.'
'Do you want a cup of tea?'
'I don't know.'
'Do you want to go to Alton Towers?'
'I don't know. What?'
'I take that as a no then.'
'No!'

Adam Eccles (9)
Harcourt Primary School

A Spiral Goes

A spiral goes round and round.
A spiral makes you dizzy.
A spiral spins like a whirlpool.
A spiral goes out of control.
A spiral keeps on going and going and going . . .

Oliver Simpson (10)
Harcourt Primary School

THERE WAS AN OLD LADY

There was an old lady
Whose cafe was bare
So she called for the dog
Saying 'Time for some air.'

She sent him to buy her
A basket of peas,
But the dog crept back
With a basket of fleas.

She sent him to buy her
A packet of frog,
But the dog jumped back
With a very long log.

She sent him to buy her
A bit of marrow,
But the dog strutted back
With a bow and arrow.

She sent him to buy her
A bowl of grapes,
But the dog scampered back
With a packet of tapes.

She sent him to buy her
A slice of beef,
But the dog ran back
With a packet of teeth.

The cupboard was bulging
And so was the fridge
So she sent for another
And walked back along a bridge.

Carly-Anne Dowsett (9)
Harcourt Primary School

TINA CHAIR

Tina Chair
Tina Chair
The only girl I've seen to stare.

Seen to stare
Seen to stare
Does Tina Chair.

Tina Chair
Tina Chair
The only girl with messy hair.

Messy hair
Messy hair
Has Tina Chair.

Silly old Tina Chair.

Bethia Coady-Mayall (10)
Harcourt Primary School

BLUE

Blue is a sea colour that crashes on the shore.
Blue is a very cold colour.
Blue is a sky colour.
Blue is part of a firework that bangs in the sky.
Blue is a pen colour that you write with.
Blue is a sheet that you put over your motorbike.

Ross Godden (9)
Harcourt Primary School

THERE WAS AN OLD WOMAN

There was an old woman
Whose kitchen was bare
So she called for the cat
Saying time for some air.

She sent him to buy her
A box of cakes
But the cat ran back
With a small lake.

She sent him to buy her
A basket of beans
But the cat hurried back
With a vacuum cleaner.

The fridge was soon bulging
And so was the shelf
So she sent for a hot curry
And ate it herself.

Robert Jenner (9)
Harcourt Primary School

RAIN

Drops spitting
from the steely sky,
glittering from puddles,
we huddle up tight together.
It is bitter outside
rain getting arctic
by minutes.
Spatter!

Leasha Donnelly (11)
Harcourt Primary School

Untitled

Seven happy children
Picking up some sticks
One pokes his eye out
Then there were six.

Six clever children
Eating lovely chives
One feels sick
Then there were five.

Five big children
Sitting on the shore
One was washed away
Then there were four.

Four quiet children
Down at the sea
One was drowned
Then there were three.

Three noisy children
Buying something new
One got lost in a shop
Then there were two.

Two lovely children
Playing in the sun
One got sunburnt
Then there was one.

One small child
Feeling all alone
Decided to watch television
So then he went home.

Jacob Coady-Mayall (7)
Harcourt Primary School

UNTITLED

One lonely child
Lost her shoe
A helpful person came along
Then there were two.

Two happy children
Climbing up a tree
Another climbed up
Then there were three.

Three silly children
Opening the door
One more came along
Then there were four.

Four lucky children
Just above to dive
The instructor came along
Then there were five.

Five messy children
Eating a Twix
Another child came along
Then there were six.

Six happy children
Going to Devon
They met another child
Then there were seven.

Seven happy children
Playing with a plate
Another came along
Then there were eight.

Jasmin Louise Cowdroy (8)
Harcourt Primary School

FIVE THIN CHILDREN

Five thin children
Playing with a door
One gets his finger trapped
Then there were four.

Four happy children
Playing with a bee
One got stung and ran away
Then there were three.

Three hiding children
Jumped out and yelled, boo!
The little one ran away
Then there were two.

Two smiling children
Lying in the sun
One got fizzled up
Then there was one.

Warren Denman (7)
Harcourt Primary School

RAIN

Drops spitting
from the steely sky.
The glittering puddles.
We huddle up tight together.
It is bitter outside.
Rain getting Arctic by minutes.
Spatter!

Natasha Stitson (11)
Harcourt Primary School

UNTITLED

Seven big children
All in a fix
One fell over
Then there were six.

Six smiling children
Learning to dive
One sunk like a stone
Then there were five.

Five tiny children
Playing around a door
One hurt her fingers
Then there were four.

Four Harcourt children
Sitting in a tree
One fell out
Then there were three.

Three little children
Tying up their shoe
One did it in knots
Then there were two.

Two big children
Were having fun
He went home
Then there was one.

One lonely child
Laying in bed
He fell out
Then there were none.

Rachael Martin (8)
Harcourt Primary School

UNTITLED

Seven tiny children
Eating a Twix
One got run over
Then there were six.

Six pale children
Going for a dive
One drowned
Then there were five.

Five lonely children
Painting a door
One fell over
Then there were four.

Four silly children
Sitting near a tree
One climbed up
Then there were three.

Three sad children
Tying up their shoe
One tripped up
Then there were two.

Two stupid children
Playing on a drum
One banged his finger
And then there was one.

Lisa Wilson (8)
Harcourt Primary School

ONE TO SEVEN

One lonely football boy
Tying up his shoe
Michael Owen came along
Then there were two.

Two happy children
Skipping near a tree
Luke Spence jumped in
Then there were three.

Three shivering children
Sitting on the floor
Stephanie gave them cushions
Then there were four.

Four hungry children
Sitting near a hive
Samuel got some honey
Then there were five.

Five nursery children
Sitting with some bricks
Danny helped to build a tower
Then there were six.

Six splashing children
Swimming down to Devon
Warren dived right in
Then there were seven.

Danny Richmond (8)
Harcourt Primary School

RAIN IS AN ACTOR

Rain is an actor
hanging from the stage ceiling
singing high and low pitch.

Rain is entertaining
with its dancing and singing
the rain takes your breath away.

Rain has gone
ready for the next show
so bye rain and good luck.

The drizzle of the rain
is music to my ears
the rain is fast or can be unhurried.

Harold Arnold (11)
Harcourt Primary School

UNTITLED

Inwards or outwards rotation from the core or edge
Curling, twirling, swirl, whirl and curl,
Wind down and down to the floor
From tornadoes to shells, whirl and whirl, curl and curl.
But where did it come from?
Italy, Greece or Rome?
What's its word origin?
'Spira' or curl?
Which is which?
What is what?
Ever wondered about spirals?

Ashley Wells (11)
Harcourt Primary School

THE FORM OF A RAINBOW

Across the bridge as we run
Drop, drop one by one.
Still we are followed by the cantering horses.
Finally safe at home
Leaving the horses out to roam
Looking out the window
Is the rain going to stop?
Drip, drip, drop, drop
Is the rain calming down
Or is it going to be a flooded town?
Slowly the sun appears
It forms a rainbow
Then the rain began to go.

Christiana Cridland (10)
Harcourt Primary School

RAIN, THUNDER AND WIND

As the rain clouds gallop and trot
Across the dark sky, the wind howls through the trees.
Thunder echoes through the house and
lightning strikes like a light bulb.
The wind blows your hair like you've had an electric shock.
Children stand in the wind shivering.
I am waiting by the windowpane.
Waiting for it to stop.
Drip, drop goes the rain, down it goes.

Sarah Louise Bliss (10)
Harcourt Primary School

UNTITLED

Seven little children
Picking up sticks
One poked his eye out
Then there were six.

Six little children
Learning how to dive
One sank like a stone
Then there were five.

Five little children
Opening a door
It closed on one
Then there were four.

Four little children
Climbing a tree
One fell off
Then there were three.

Three little children
Went to the loo
One flushed the chain
Then there were two.

Two little children
Sitting in the sun
One got burnt
Then there was one.

One little child
Laying in bed
Got so lonely
Fell out of bed.

Charlotte Lund (8)
Harcourt Primary School

Untitled

Seven little children
Eating a Twix
One stuffed it in too fast, bang!
And then there were six.

Six little children
Playing near a beehive
The bees came out
And then there were five.

Five little children
Knocking at a door
One fell in
Then there were four.

Four little children
Getting something for free
One got lost
Then there were three.

Three little children
Buying something new
One went home crying
Then there were two.

Two little children
Playing in the sun
One got burnt
Then there was one.

One little child
Feeling all alone
Decided to watch TV
And so he went home.

***Daniel Howarth (8)**
Harcourt Primary School*

THERE WAS AN OLD GEEZER

There was an old geezer
Whose kitchen was bare
So he sent for his mouse
To get some fresh air.

So he sent her to buy
A lump of fish
But the mouse trotted back
With a magical wish.

So he sent her to buy him
A lot of ham
But the mouse sprinted back
With a big leg of lamb.

So he sent her to buy him
A smelly dead rat
But instead he ran back
With an old welcome mat.

The fridge was soon bulging
And so was the shelf
So he got all these things
All alone by himself.

Dean Richmond (10)
Harcourt Primary School

UNTITLED

Spirals are like ammonite twisting round and round.
Spirals are like a staircase stepping down and down.
Spirals are like whirlpools that gather up the winds.

Daisy Fordham (10)
Harcourt Primary School

NOISE

I like noise.
The noise and smells of the city.
The pollution what's the solution?
Red double decker buses, red and pretty.
Tower block floors higher and higher,
The shouting of people in lifts.
The taxis beeping the cars,
The slam of doors,
The munching of people in cafes,
The cries of babies in prams,
The roar of traffic pulling up,
The red, amber and green traffic lights,
The flashing of lights in clubs.

Megan Morris (10)
Hextable Junior School

NOISE

I like noise
The hoot of an owl, the squeak of a guinea pig,
The gobble of a turkey, the chirp of a bird,
The bark of a dog, the snort of a pig,
The bleat of a deer, the snuffle of a rabbit,
The hiss of a snake, the purr of a cat,
The laugh of a hyena, the roar of a lion,
The chatter of a monkey, the trumpeting of the elephant,
The buzz of the bee, the cry of a dolphin in danger,
The howl of a wolf, the baa of a sheep.
I like noise.

Kathryn Sutton (10)
Hextable Junior School

NOISE

Noise is brilliant,
The roar of a car as it revs into gear,
The rat-a-tat-tat of a woodpecker making its home,
The continuous din of a plane's propeller,
The crack of lightning, the boom of thunder,
The blast of a laser in a space movie,
The slam of a heavy fire door,
The silence-shattering howl of a baby,
The tremendous boom of a drum,
The blare of a trumpet,
The crack of a rifle in a rifle range,
The splash of someone diving into a pool,
The rattling of hail bouncing off a tin roof,
The snap of a crocodile's jaw, the laughing of a hyena.
I like noise.

Ben Lawrence (9)
Hextable Junior School

NOISE

I like noise.
The boom of a bomb, the roar of a train.
The rattle of a snake, the click of a light.
The howl of a wolf, the screech of a mouse.
The rumble of the sky, the clank of a chain.
The slam of a door, the conk of an engine.
The smash of glass, the crush of cars.
The cry of a cat, the scream of an F1 car,
The bark of a dog, the beep of a horn.
I like noise.

Aaron Farmer (10)
Hextable Junior School

FISH

I like noise.

The whoosh of a fish,
The flap if its fins,
The tiny tank in which it lives,
The drone of a heater,
The flap of its fins,
The zoom of the school.

The whip of its tale,
The boy who keeps tapping the tank,
The other fish flap their fins and zoom around,
While the sucker fish cleans up and down.

Ben Nazarjuk (9)
Hextable Junior School

ANIMAL NOISES

I like noise.
The noise of a dog, the miaow of a cat,
The tweet of a budgie, the squeak of a guinea pig,
The gobble of a turkey, quack of a duck,
The croak of a frog, the trot of a horse,
The moo of a cow, the cluck of a chicken,
The grunt of a pig, the chat of a human,
The squeak of a mouse, the buzz of a bee,
The hoot of an owl, the coo of a pigeon,
The sniffing of a rabbit, the growl of a bear.
I like noise.

Lynsey White (10)
Hextable Junior School

LOOKING OUT MY MISTY WINDOW

Looking out my misty window
I can see a lonely old man
sweeping roads. Slowly sweeping
the snow away.

Looking out my misty window
I can see a carriage.
A horse making deep tracks
in the snow.

Looking out my misty window,
snow starts falling heavily.
It covers up the tracks
and footprints.

Looking out my misty window,
a sheet of white has covered
the pavement. People are coming out of
their houses making new footprints.

Looking out my misty window,
I can see children coming
out of their houses. Running fast
to the park to start throwing snowballs.

I prefer it in here, warm
by the fire where leaping flames fly,
red, yellow, orange and gold with a
hot mug of tea in my hand.

Sian Birleson (9)
Hextable Junior School

OUT IN THE OPEN

Outside the ground is like a huge white sheet
Covering the trees that crack their fingers.
The ground is soft and smooth.

Hedges are freezing, my feet are ice cubes.
My tongue is out to catch a snowflake.
Something just dropped, it was cold.

I struggle through the albino snow,
and watch the swirling stillness grow.
Snow bees settle in the tree and
Snow moths on the gate.

The cattle's breath, in rags it hangs.
The windows are steamed up.
Puddles are shimmering, frost is forming quickly.

Stray cats shiver on the wall.
My chilblains are itching badly.
Bare trees are looking sulky.
The sun is very pale.

Roads are slipping with the ice.
The ice is clear and hard.
The snow is thick and frosty.
I wish this white sheet would blow away.

Inside a house it is warm and cosy.
The fire is blazing with light.
I sit in a comfy chair and think how cosy.

Emma Kirby (9)
Hextable Junior School

WINTER

F lakes coming down on to the ground.
R acing river all frozen over.
O n every roof there is snow.
S warming frost flakes in the trees.
T racks of feet in the snow.
Y ou would have to wear a thick coat.

C old, windy, wet weather.
O n every tree there is snow.
L ots of snow covering the ground.
D ead plants everywhere.

W aving trees in the wind.
I cy, windy weather.
N ow everyone is very cold.
T icking clocks inside.
E verything is covered in a blanket of snow.
R ed flames in the fire.

W et, windy weather.
E ach snowflakes is coming down on to the ground.
A ll things are covered in white.
T iny, sparkling snowflakes.
H ot, burning fire.
E veryone is wearing warm coats.
R ed, gold flames coming out of the fire.

Natalie Clough (9)
Hextable Junior School

SNOWFLAKES

Outside the whole
garden was covered
with snow.

The spiders' webs that
hung there the night before
had turned to silver.

Icicles hanging off
the top of
roofs.

Children skating
on ice, children
having snowball fights.

Snowflakes were
dancing around
in my head.

Then snowflakes
started to fall
outside they made me sleepy.

Carly Fordham (10)
Hextable Junior School

THE FOOTBALL MATCH

I like noise.

The shouting and screaming
from the crowd.
A player gets fouled and the booing begins.
A man from the crowd shouts, 'Ref are you blind?'

A player scores with an overhead kick
and the crowd goes wild shouting, cheering
and booing from the crowd and the shouting
from the away keeper.

I like noise.

Craig Strachan (10)
Hextable Junior School

JACK FROST

Jack Frost comes in winter.
He is after our fingers and toes.
He makes patterns on the windows.
He makes trails like winter snails.
Sparkly snowflakes fall.

They cover the grass and
freeze the lakes and fish cannot escape.
The powdery snow is so thick it would meet your knees.
The white powdery snow is good to play in.
The icy roads are dangerous.

People wear thick coats and big boots.
Children have numb fingers.
Everyone has chunky jumpers.
Central heating in people's houses.
It keeps them warm in winter.

The trees are leafless.
The powdery snow falls on branches.
Animals are hibernating in them.
The robin comes in winter
and everyone loves him.

Aaron Cook (10)
Hextable Junior School

SNOW ON A WINTER'S DAY

S now on a winter's day.
N obody walking the streets.
O utside is still, just the cold, chilly snow falling gently.
W hile I'm watching and waiting for the snow to finish falling.

O utside looks as if no one has discovered it.
N obody is going out in this cold weather.

A stray cat wanders the street alone, shivering, shivering.

W hen winter arrives there's no one outside.
I suppose everyone is stuck at home.
N ature's animals all outside looking for food.
T rudging through the snow.
E very day seems like a new life.
R esting and hoping the snow will finish falling.
S now, snow, snow.

D ays of snow
A nd ice
Y ou will not want to be out in the snow.

Rosemary Haward (9)
Hextable Junior School

THE ICE MAN

Round the dark corner of the street, whistling sounds
can be heard in the air. A man walks along
the black, black road, as cold as ice.
Walking slowly as his feet crackle on the pavement.

The houses are as still as rocks and the children
are throwing snowballs and making snowmen.
The lonely man still walks on the scattered snow.
His head shaking like albino white.
Children still laughing while building the snowmen.

One old detached house standing on its own
trying to say something. It must be extremely warm
in there, sitting by that cosy fire,
thinking about the hot summer days.

The trees and bushes standing there,
lingering for the ice man to walk past them.
The ice man goes, goes to the door as still as stone.
Will he be going to go in?

Nathan Morris (9)
Hextable Junior School

FROM MY WINDOW I CAN SEE...

From my window I can see
Icy snowflakes float to the ground.
I can see a white sheet of snow
Covering the ground.

And birds are flying by.
From my window I can see
A robin on a tree.
I stare and stare.

I can see my dad trying
To start his car.
A dog is walking by my window
With a red and green coat on.

He is making footprints in the snow.
The snow keeps on falling and the
Footprints are covered with crisp new snow.
I can see children making a snowman.

I look and look and look.

Gemma Chuter (10)
Hextable Junior School

CELEBRATIONS 2000

We are going to stay up till midnight,
To celebrate the second millennium,
We'll dance to music and play games,
Make a bonfire and have fireworks too,
We could eat and drink all we like,
And organise quizzes also.

Some of my friends are going on holiday,
To celebrate the second millennium,
They might go skiing or swimming,
Or maybe go to the beach,
They could stay in a hotel or rent a flat,
Or they might go camping also.

Some people will visit the Dome,
To celebrate the second millennium.
They might start to make and get tattoos
For no reason at all
But to have a good time and to mark a new
chapter in their lives.

James Wyatt (10)
Hextable Junior School

CELEBRATION 2000

The millennium is coming
There will be parties everywhere.
What will you be doing
To welcome in that special year?

Will you be jetting off to Barbados
Roasting in the sun?
Or will you be sloping off to the Alps
Skiing into everyone?

For me the answer is quite clear -
On the stroke of midnight I'll leave all the cheer.
I'll give Mum and Dad a very quick hug,
'Sorry, I'm off to catch the Millennium Bug!'

Richard Brown (11)
Hextable Junior School

I Look Outside

I look outside and I can see
a winter wasteland full of snow
and ice.

A horse and carriage draw near the window.
The horse is snorting steam from its nostrils.
Icy puddles gleam in the light.

Icy patterns fall from the gloomy, grey sky.
Children my age have fun with the snow.

I have chilblains that itch like mad.
Will summer ever come?
Under this vast white sheet is there life?

Clouds are spreading like cotton wool all over the grey sky.
A pale pastel sun sets in the gloomy sky.

Bare trees fill the forest.
I have to plod through thick mud to get to the barn.

I go home and rest by the warm fire.
My cat is sitting by my side yawning.
I go to my warm bed and lie down.
How warm it is.

Emma Hamilton-Jenkins (10)
Hextable Junior School

NOISE

I like noise.
The rattle of the snake.
The clattering hooves of horses' feet.
The trumpeting of elephants like an army.
The screeching of parrots coming down.
The fierce tiger growling wherever he goes.
The gobbling and munching noises of sharks eating fish.
The hooting sounds which owls make at night.
The tough bear beating the honey tree.
The stampede of wild beasts rushing like a gush of wind.
The roar of a lion like crashing thunder coming down.
The laughing of hyenas like a small boy.
The chatter of monkeys as they swing from tree to tree.
The buzzing sounds of bees like people humming.
I like noise.

Sachin Wadher (10)
Hextable Junior School

MILLENNIUM

The millennium is a great time for everyone
People shouting and cheering in London
For the new generation
Night-time will be full of flashes,
Fireworks which will light up the
Sky with sparks and colours,
New inventions have begun for everyone,
And millennium is a great celebration
For everyone.

Robert Bennett (10)
Hextable Junior School

A Snowy Day

Crisp, bitter snow underfoot.
Snowballs flying around.

No gentle chatter of the birds
singing in the trees.

Wind that seems like a gale
knocks slates off roofs.

Cat prints in the snow.
School carpets covered in slush.

Snowmen being knocked down.
Ice covers the pond.

I go inside the house.
The windows are all misty.

Outside lamps are glowing.
Frost is gathering on our car.

It is starting to rain.
My cat is coming in.

Wet and soggy.
Drying by the fire.

Soon it's time for bed.
Climbing up the stairs.

Rebecca Carpenter (10)
Hextable Junior School

SNOW

Snow, snow everywhere,
soft as silk, as cold as ice.
Fun to play in.
Far too cold to stay in.
When I look outside
I wish the snow was
in not out.
Oh I wish winter
would never, ever end.
Snow forever.
Paradise for me.
I would play in it every day.
Then after playing in the
snow all day,
go and have
my roast dinner
by the blazing fire
of red, yellow, gold and orange.
Then go to bed
of warmth and safety
and dream of the
crystal-white snow.

Darrell Baker (10)
Hextable Junior School

A WINTER'S NIGHT IN LONDON

At night Trafalgar Square is quite a sight.
Lights flash, the moon glows, cold
Wind blows in Trafalgar Square at night.

Oxford Street, a good place for shopping.
Shoppers stroll to Hamleys. Bold, cold weather,
Gloves and hat worn in Oxford Street at night.

Nelson's Column covered in snow.
It's a good place for pigeons to go.
London nightlife in winter, that's the place I would go.

Sam Luchford (10)
Hextable Junior School

CELEBRATION 2000

Parties are being thrown all over London,
People are dressing up in fancy costumes,
Fancy clothes,
Lots to eat.

In other countries the same is happening,
Everybody's getting ready to dance,
People eating,
Dancing, drinking.

When the party's just about to begin,
Everyone's outside in a queue,
Lining up,
Very quiet.

In the middle of the party,
Every person is dancing to marvellous music,
Music loud,
Nearly sweated out.

At the end of the party,
Everyone's had a good time,
Drunk and full,
Stomachs hurting,
Headaches pounding.

Nick Self (10)
Hextable Junior School

A Frozen Winter

A snowman in the garden.

F rost is settling on the ground.
R oads all slippery, cars skidding.
O n the trees there is snow.
Z ig zag icicles hanging from houses.
E mpty streets outside our house.
N obody will go out in this weather.

W hile I am waiting for the snow to finish falling
I just sit and wait by the window sill.
N ew snow falls on old snow covering the footprints.
T rees all bare with no leaves on them.
E verybody is sitting by the warm fires.
R esting and waiting for the snow to finish falling.

James Culliford (9)
Hextable Junior School

Celebration 2000

A new start,
Another new year, a special one this time,
Here comes a new century,
The millennium is here,
The year 2000 we all cheer,
People having fun and lots of parties going on,
The Millennium Dome is opened,
I can see balloons passing in the sky,
Celebration 2000.

Michaela Read (11)
Hextable Junior School

THE NOISY FARM

I like noise.
The clank of the pail, the chirp of the chick.
The moo of the cow, the baa of the sheep.
The clonking of a tractor, the snorting of the pigs.
The slam of the gate, the swish, swash water sounds.
The rush of wind, the bark of the sheepdog.
The whistle of the farmer to the dog, the clucking of the hens.
The gnawing of the mouse, the buzzing of the bee.
The rooster shouts cock-a-doodle-do, the neigh of the horse.
The howl of the guard dog, the cry of a child visiting.
The whoosh of the child going down a slide.
The clip-clop noise from the shire horse's feet.
I like noise.

Chloe Smithers (9)
Hextable Junior School

NOISE OF ALL AROUND

I like noise.
The bark of a dog, the miaow of a cat.
The screech of chalk on a blackboard.
The bang of a bomb from World War Two.
The scream of a child, the squeak of a hamster.
The quack of a duck.
The clank of a magnet going on the freezer.
The smash of a vase falling from the shelf.
The rustling of long grass when a dog walks through.
The roar of a tiger.
The splash of water.
I like noise.

Lauren Evans (9)
Hextable Junior School

OUT OF MY FROSTED WINDOW

I wake up to see
my garden under a white blanket.
White frost sprinkled on the walls.
The trees are covered with a layer of snow
like icing.
Curtains are opened slithers with little life known.
People de-icing their cars.
I can see a worried couple
staring at their car engine.
It must be so cold outside
And it is so warm in bed.
I crawl out of bed and shuffle downstairs.
Then I see a hot chocolate sitting waiting for me.
I sip it, looking out of my frosted window and think,
how warm it is in bed.

Charlotte Phillips (10)
Hextable Junior School

CELEBRATION 2000

The Millennium Dome of Greenwich
is not very far from Woolwich.
It is full of exhibitions
to walk through is an expedition.
There will be a grand display
of video games that you love to play.
There will be the latest DIY.
Loads of tools for you to buy.
So we can look forward to a century
that people will enjoy in a land of plenty.

Adam Draper (11)
Hextable Junior School

THE NOISE OF THE BEACH

I like the noise of the beach.
The splash of waves.
The slurping of drinks.
The blowing of a lifeguard's whistle.
The munch of people eating biscuits.
The ching of a till. People buying things.
The whizzing of a jet ski in the water.
The noise of laughter enjoying the beach.
The scream of a girl being pinched by a crab.
The noise in the arcade.
The noise of traffic trying to park.
The drilling of workmen fitting in cables.
People asking for ice-cream.
I like the noise of the beach.

James Tuffee (10)
Hextable Junior School

CELEBRATION 2000

A change of mood maybe
for the new millennium.
New high-tech equipment.
Scientists coming up with better ideas
but there are problems they say like
computers crashing,
because they don't recognise 00.
Working hard to think up new inventions.
A change for your life or
a change of mood maybe?

Rachel Mole (11)
Hextable Junior School

Winter Waking

W inter with my cat calling to me.
I t is a lovely view from a window.
N ow when will the snow come out.
T all trees are silent in winter.
E ating for deer in the wild.
R ain will be here more now.

W alking down the slippy road are your feet.
A mazing patterns slashing the window.
K icking the snow all around you.
I nside is lovely and warm.
N ot knowing how you can get to school.
G ardens full of snow.

Rachel Parker (10)
Hextable Junior School

Millennium 2000

M usic and singing in the street.
I dance to the rhythm and the beat.
L aughing and talking all night long.
L oving every minute as I join in the songs.
E veryone jolly having fun.
N o one sad, the millennium has just begun.
N ightlights light up the sky
I s it possible they will dim and die.
U se your computers at your own risk.
M illennium bug may hit or miss!

George Hutchins (11)
Hextable Junior School

THE BLUE TREES

The blue trees
shivering in the
spherical moon's light.

The blue trees
waving their icy branches
in the bitter, biting wind.

The blue trees
freeze on their shadows.
Will they ever see the sun again?

The blue trees
are stationary on the field.
Not allowed to come into the
glowing warmth of the house.

In the house
the silence of the sleeping family
is so warm you can almost hear it.

In the house
the fire is burning
red, yellow, orange and gold.

In the house,
the windowpane is misted up
and when we come to clean it
we will see the blue trees
standing there alone.

Sarah Crouch (10)
Hextable Junior School

CELEBRATION 2000

The clock strikes twelve
one year ends and another one approaches.
The crowds pour into Trafalgar Square and Piccadilly Circus.
Wine bottles pop.
Babies cry.
An old man dies.
Another year approaches.
A thousand years have gone by
in the blink of an eye
and we did not even notice.
Will the world change?
Will the church bells ring?
People starving in this world,
will they be fed and will the people on the
streets get a home and will these answers be in
the Millennium Dome!
Now we have got to celebrate.
The year 2000 is here.
Happy faces everywhere
all full of cheer.
Let there be peace and no war.
That's what I would choose if it was up to me.
That is what the next millennium should bring
and I hope it is something I'll get to see.
But it is still 1999
so we've got a bit more time
until the millennium is here.

Debbie Stoner (11)
Hextable Junior School

CELEBRATION 2000

Here comes another year
but this year it's special
it's the year 2000.
A new year, a new decade, a new century, a
new millennium.
Clashing of champagne glasses, popping of
party poppers.
Tears of happiness, laughs of joy, singing and
dancing all night long.
We'll fight the Millennium Bug and fight for peace
and hope the world to be a better place.
People thinking of robots to do their chores.
Washing, mowing and taking over.
Flying cars, hover bikes, people living on the moon.
An imaginary world which might even come.
New machinery, new places like the
Millennium Dome.
A place where children will learn and play.
10, 9, 8, 7, 6, 5, 4, 3, 2, 1
It's the moment we've been waiting for year 2000!
A once in a lifetime experience we'll see with
our eyes.
Big Ben striking at twelve o'clock
*Ding, dong, ding, dong, ding, dong, ding, dong,
ding, dong, ding, dong.*
People crying, 'Happy New Year!'

Martyn Searles (11)
Hextable Junior School

CELEBRATION 2000

We're at the end of '99,
A time to celebrate,
With discos and parties we all have fun.
The second millennium's almost begun.

New technology every day,
There's such a lot to learn.
Now we can surf the Internet,
How much better can it get?

The biggest event ever known,
Is just about to start.
The new year's party that'll beat them all,
With dancing and fireworks, it'll be so cool.

I can't wait till the year 2000,
I know it will be such fun.
I'd like to see the Millennium Dome.
Then after that I'd hate to come home!

Christina Monti (10)
Hextable Junior School

CELEBRATION 2000

2000, 2000 this is the year
that life will truly begin.
There'll be shouts and cheers
with barrels of beer for everyone to enjoy.
They will have buildings and sites
where people will delight
and have years being happy and glad.

Ben Samuel (11)
Hextable Junior School

CELEBRATION 2000!

Millennium is coming.
it's time to celebrate.
For here comes
the year 2000!

It's the millennium.
Computers are having problems.
With this virus called
The Millennium Bug.

The Millennium Bug,
confuses our
computers by changing
their dates.

The Millennium Dome
will not be finished.
Because the workers are too slow.

Philip Donkersley (10)
Hextable Junior School

CELEBRATION

F is for the fun the new millennium will bring.
U is for the unknown that is in store for us.
T is for the time ticking by.
U is for uproarious party we will have at the turn of the century.
R is for the relatives we will be celebrating the new century with.
E is for the emotions we will be feeling with the passing
of the old century.

Joe Sandford (10)
Hextable Junior School

The Angry Millennium Dome

I'm new so now nobody will talk to me,
It's like I'm in a new school.
Yes! buildings do have feelings.
I'm sitting here waiting for someone to talk to me.
I'm alone and talking to myself.
I'm unhappy because they are talking behind my walls,
I have no say to what happens to me.
I'm not even allowed to move around.
Ochh ohh, here they go again jabbing their tools into me,
I cannot take it anymore.
They use me to do experiments on, I feel like a lab rat.
People put rods into me and they walk on my mosaic floors.
They have done nothing nice to me yet,
But they do polish my floor and paint my windows.
So I suppose I should stand up straight,
But only on condition they talk to me.
Ohh and praise the Lord, here comes millions of people talking to me,
So now I can stand up straight and start acting nice
And glisten in the sun.

Edele Barnett (11)
Hextable Junior School

Poem On Party 2000

P eople such as mums kissing little children.
A ll of the adults dancing to the music.
R ound a friend's house having a party.
T ime to count down until midnight.
Y ou and me dancing all night.

Bradley Freeman (11)
Hextable Junior School

CELEBRATION 2000

Ding dong,
Big Ben chiming in the year 2000,
The second millennium since Jesus was born.

2000 years since Jesus' birth,
Now we lead a very different life to them,
Many devices we have, they didn't even dream of.

A futuristic phase in time could lead to:
Motorised skateboards,
Computerised fridges,
Even school classes on the Internet.

Do you think the year 2000 will be a peaceful, enjoyable year?
Do you reckon the world will change much, or not?

Alex Ward (10)
Hextable Junior School

CELEBRATION 2000

The millennium is here,
Let's all give a cheer,
Banners everywhere,
Celebration's in the air,
The party is swinging,
The bells are ringing,
To celebrate the new year!

Jade Wright (11)
Hextable Junior School

CELEBRATION 2000

The clock strikes twelve, we say goodbye to our old millennium and enter the new one.
Music is thumping loudly and everyone is having a good time.
Everyone is joking and laughing, the world is partying wildly.
Little children are even awake (although on a normal night they would be in bed).
The sun is awakening and we are in our first day of the millennium.
Parents and children go to bed suffering from headaches.
Everyone is happy (although they might be in pain)
and the moon goes to bed.

Jeb Lynch (10)
Hextable Junior School

CELEBRATION 2000

Celebration 2000 is when sparks burst to the sky,
Celebration 2000 is when rockets shoot sky high.

Celebration 2000 is when unique doors open,
Celebration 2000 is the time of the new millennium.

Celebration 2000 is when the Earth completes its turn,
Celebration 2000 is when the fire of prosperity still burns.

Christopher Blanchard (11)
Hextable Junior School

CELEBRATION 2000

C elebrating the millennium
E venings seem longer as the night gets closer
L oneliness for some people in poorer parts of the world
E verlasting parties to celebrate the forthcoming year
B eer and wine to last a lifetime
R emembering how lucky we are at this time of year
A t twelve o'clock Big Ben starts the parties for everyone in England
T rying to forget the bad things that happened in 1999
I ndividuals still partying at four o'clock in the morning
O ccasionally topping up people's glasses
N ow the party is over, adults inspect the damage of the party as the children go to bed.

Amelia Bushell (11)
Hextable Junior School

CELEBRATION 2000

The millennium year is here
On 31st December 1999 when Big Ben strikes 12 o'clock
Everybody raises their glasses which are full of wine
Which clatter in the air
There will be shouts and cheers everywhere you go
There will be sparks from fireworks flying all around you
And it is the start of a new millennium.

Ricky Bullimore (11)
Hextable Junior School

INTO THE CASTLE OF THE BARONESS JUGULA

The gates are smelly and crumbly
And dead flowers over the wall
I walked to the door
For my meeting with the Baroness

Knotted wood and rusty handle
My hands began to tremble
I ring the bell not once but twice
And how I looked in such a surprise
And there before me stood
A woman with a touch of motherhood
A glass of lemonade in her hand
A warm welcome and a gentle smile
My fears, my worried looks
Am I grateful it's my nan.

Karina Cork (9)
Knockholt CE Primary School

DIRTY OLD BILL

There was an old man
Who lived on a hill
He never never washed
And he never never will
If he's not dead
He's living there still
His funny old name was
Dirty Old Bill.

Callum McDonald (7)
Knockholt CE Primary School

LET'S PLAY FOOTBALL

Shall we play?
Let's play football.
Look, it's a lovely day.
You can be in goal,
you can kick the ball high.
It's much more fun than going for a stroll.
Let's play football.
I'll take a corner.
All this running around is making me warmer!
Don't get a red card.
This game is getting hard.
Let's play football.

Arron Smart (7)
Knockholt CE Primary School

SIMILE

The sun is like a middle of a daisy.
The world spins round like a football.
A fairy is like confetti.
The colour red is like danger.
A stormy night is like a spooky ride.
A giant is like an earthquake when it stops.
The colour pink is like flowers.
Ice is like candy sugar.
Flowers are like perfume.
Fire is like hot chocolate.
Snow is like ice-cream.

Kate Morris (9)
Knockholt CE Primary School

THE DEN OF THE WICKED WITCH

I came out of the brightly lit room,
into the gloomy corridor
and as I walked the darkness deepened.
The walls felt damp and cold,
now something scuttled past me unseen,
now a strange smell made my nose twitch,
now a cobweb brushed across my face,
now I started to tremble with fear,
now I thought 'Why me? Oh why me?'
as I found the door to my doom and knocked
and an eerie voice cackled 'Come into my den.'

The door creaked slowly open
and I could not move at all,
then my shaking legs started to move at last.
My courage returned in the wicked witch's den,
where I looked into the old crone's eyes and said
'Here's the assembly book, headmistress.'

Lorna Tester (8)
Knockholt CE Primary School

I WISH I HAD A MONKEY

I wish I had a monkey
to come and play with me
I think it would be very funky
if he could come to tea
We would have some jelly
then watch some telly
Oh I wish I had a monkey
to come and play with me.

Ellie Fay Gatsell (8)
Knockholt CE Primary School

TO THE CASTLE OF BARONESS JUGULA

There are no bushes and trees
There's only one flower but it's mostly just weeds
But I went there once for a dare
I went to the Castle of Baroness Jugula
Past savage bungee-jumping hounds which snapped at my head
Past ten circular saws that came up from the ground
Right up to the door where I knocked
And the door swung open to reveal
The gruesome, loathsome face of Baroness Jugula
Then I said
'Can I have my yo-yo back?'

Tom Hinks (9)
Knockholt CE Primary School

I'M HAVING FUN

I'm having fun
Dragons are toasting my burger in a bun
Red, yellow and green
The best at cooking you've ever seen
Bloodeye, Toothfang and Marleybone
I could never say I feel alone
I'm having fun
Toothfang is always on the run
Marleybone is the cooker
And Bloodeye, he's the best reader
I'm having fun.

Gemma Cakebread (9)
Knockholt CE Primary School

I Am An Island Stuck In The Middle Of The Sea

I am an island stuck in the middle of the sea
Some people greet me
Some people leave me
But I am still an island stuck in the middle of the sea.

Katie Gettins (9)
Knockholt CE Primary School

Warwick

There once was a boy called Yarrick
Who spent a weekend in Warwick
He bought a huge sword
For when he was bored
And he felt incredibly historic.

Samuel Shaw (8)
Knockholt CE Primary School

There Was A Young Lady

There was a young lady called Rosie
Who was feeling incredibly dozy
But when her mum said
'You'd be best off in bed'
She said 'No thanks, I'm really quite cosy.'

Rosie Kelly (9)
Knockholt CE Primary School

IS IT A GHOST?

From the living room up the stairs
and suddenly something went hoot.
Is it a ghost?
No, it's just an owl.
From the stairs to the hall
and suddenly something went flop.
Is it a ghost?
No, it's just the curtains.
From the hall to the bedroom
and suddenly something went rustle.
Is it a ghost?
No, it's just the bedclothes.
From the door to the cupboard
and open the door.
Oh no, it's a ghost!

Christopher Cheeseman (9)
Knockholt CE Primary School

BUGS

Yummy, yummy, yummy
I got bugs in my tummy
And I feel like another one
Bugs, bugs everywhere
Now I feel really queer
Bugs, bugs
On the table, on the chair
Bug spray!
Run, run bugs!

Suki Marie Clark (7)
Knockholt CE Primary School

LOVELY FISH

Fish, fish, lovely fish
Nice to eat
Nice to smell
Cod fish
Nice to eat
Nice to smell
Fish, fish, lovely fish.

Charles Robson (8)
Knockholt CE Primary School

BREAKFAST FOR ONE

Crispy, sizzling, salty bacon
With runny, yolky, crunchy egg
Sizzling bacon, crispy and yolky
Crunchy and runny egg
Washed down with juicy
Sweet and tangy orange juice.

Jessica Ann Gibbons (8)
Knockholt CE Primary School

THE MOTORBIKES

We have motorbikes,
They go very fast.
My sister and I go flying past.
We race along to the end of the lane,
Then we start all over again.

Laura Copeland (8)
Knockholt CE Primary School

THE BEACH

Walking along the beach
I hear the sea splashing
The wind blowing
Children making sandcastles
Walking along the beach
Dogs barking
Mums calling children from the sea
Walking along the beach.

Matthew Shackleton (8)
Knockholt CE Primary School

YUM CHOCOLATE YUM

Chocolate is good
Soft and silky
Chocolate is fun
Crispy and milky
Cadbury's Milk
Or a plain Flyte
Whatever type gives
You great delight.

Chad Williams (8)
Knockholt CE Primary School

A Walk In The Dark

As we got ready for a walk in the dark,
it just seemed to me as a very big park.
I walked through the door,
but I wasn't very sure.
We walked through the woods,
it was cold, so we put up our hoods.
My torch had a very bright shine,
so really I was fine.
We looked around
until we found
oh no, snakes!
Then suddenly something breaks,
but thankfully it was only a stick,
in the mud that is very thick.
Later as we got further on in the walk
it got colder so it was harder to talk.
Near the end, the mud started to squelch,
squelch, squelch, squelch,
but then we had finished,
we had done it.

Liesel Cleaver (11)
Launcelot Primary School

THE THING

It creeps around a night
waiting to give you a fright!
If you step out of bed,
it will hit you on the head.
As soon as you turn off the light,
it will be ready for a fight.
A little boy was killed in bed,
there's no such thing as monsters he said.
As you can see, he was wrong,
so stay tucked in tight,
all night long.

Dalia Awad (10)
Launcelot Primary School

SPOTS, SPOTS

Spots, spots, on a white dog.
Spots, spots, on a black and white dog.
Early in the morning
and as thin as can be,
as fat as can be.
There are black and brown spots
as large as can be, as small as can be.
I saw a lot of dogs with black and brown spots.

Scott Hazle (10)
Launcelot Primary School

IT'S TIME TO TELL YOU

It's time to tell you about a
secret I keep,
nobody knows this but me.
I can't wait for the long day to end,
so then you will see
how much you mean to me.
I close my eyes, you're by my side,
don't judge the past babe, it's only history.
I want to be yours.
It's time to tell you about a
secret I keep,
nobody knows this but me.
It might sound strange,
but I pictured us alone.
Every night I pray that there will be a way
we can make it last forever.

Jenna Ganney (11)
Launcelot Primary School

ME

I am a girl,
a girl I am.
My name is Sara.
I sit in a pan,
the pan is Fred.
The pan sits in the dustbin lid,
the dustbin lid is Paul. Paul sits
in the baby cot, the cot is Ben.
Ben is their friend.

Sara McDermott (10)
Launcelot Primary School

CELEBRATING THE MILLENNIUM

Ten, nine, eight, seven, six, five,
four, three, two, one.
Twelve o'clock strikes,
it is 01.01.2000 at last.

Everyone cheers, party poppers bang,
champagne corks pop,
some are ready to drop.

Everyone hugging and kissing,
the millennium is here.

So much planning,
I hope this millennium brings peace, no hunger,
cures for deadly illnesses,
and Manchester United for the League.

Gareth Taylor (11)
Merton Court School

CELEBRATION 2000

Hoorah! Hoorah! It's nearly New Year's Day,
the turn of the century, the year 2000.
The biggest celebration some might say.

Everybody waiting for the clock to strike,
we hope nobody will be by themselves.

No more writing 1990's in our books.
A new century is starting, so be sure to take a look.

This celebration is one to remember,
we are eagerly waiting till the end of December.

Billy Thurston (11)
Merton Court School

COUNTDOWN

Five, four, three, two, one!
The year two thousand has just begun!

Party balloons and streamers everywhere,
breathing in the new year's air.

Dancing in the street, parading around,
leaving the mess behind us on the ground!

Happy feeling drifting through the air.
Everyone free, without a worry or a care!

Soon it will be time to sleep,
we won't wake up till our alarm clocks beep!

Before we go, give a big cheer,
just to celebrate a brand new year!

Lauren Everson (10)
Merton Court School

CELEBRATION 2000

C elebrate the year 2000,
E xtravaganza parties,
L ucky to be alive,
E ngland celebrates it with the Millennium Dome,
B uried below is a time capsule,
R un around with excitement all night,
A nd wait till one second past twelve tonight,
T ime to celebrate with some pop,
I think this party is ready to rock,
O ur new millennium has just begun,
N ow it's off to bed, forget the fun.

David Williamson (10)
Merton Court School

CELEBRATION 2000

Centuries have gone since year 1000.
Entries to homes in this year.
Lots of people will be happy
at the Millennium Dome.
Brains will be better in 2000.
Radical people will come on
31st December,
an exciting event will go on.
Times have changed since year 1000.
Intriguing news will be on TV,
OAPs will be there as well.
Nothing on earth can spoil the fun.

Amit Patel (11)
Merton Court School

MILLENNIUM

Midnight has come,
celebration's begun.
Let out a cheer!
The millennium's here.
The Dome has been built,
champagne has been spilt,
let out a yell!
I can hear Big Ben's bell.
I've made a resolution,
it's my contribution.
Let out a scream!
Let your party poppers stream.

Katy Davies (10)
Merton Court School

PARTY TIME

What are people doing
on this special night.
Some are lighting candles,
some on Concorde flight.
Parties being held all over the world,
people laughing, dancing, singing
and the great bells of St Paul's are ringing.
We all hope to read aloud
the millennium resolution,
'Let there be respect for the Earth,
peace for its people,
love in our lives,
delight in the good,
forgiveness for others from past wrongs,
and from now, a new start.'

Francesca Mestre (10)
Merton Court School

CELEBRATION 2000

As we stood in Leicester Square,
everybody stood to stare at the clock which told us when
year 2000 would come,
and in its own way, it would say Happy New Year.

One minute to go,
and everyone would let the champagne spray flow.
Everyone would dance the night away,
very happily until the next day.

The year 2000, wow, wee,
the only one that I would see.
The biggest year of my life,
the one to celebrate best of all.

No one here will see another millennium,
the flashing lights,
the loud music,
as we celebrate the year 2000.

Jason Macdonald (10)
Merton Court School

CELEBRATION 2000

The year 2000 is here,
everybody gives a big cheer.
The new millennium has arrived,
great new adventures to be tried.

The fireworks are let off with a bang,
everybody shouts 'Again! Again!'
how great it is to see a new year in,
I smile with a great big grin.

Champagne's being offered around,
there's hardly any sound.
We're about to give a great big toast,
I'm looking forward to that the most.

The clock strikes twelve,
it's finally here,
we are about to start a
brand new year!

Hannah Jarmyn (10)
Merton Court School

CELEBRATION 2000

In the year 2000 we will cheer,
many people will drink beer.
I will start my secondary school
and the millennium will be so cool.
At that special second or two,
the next sound in the morning
will be the birds starting to coo.
People partying in the night
and fireworks flying in the sky.
The great Millennium Dome
will make us feel at home.
On the eve of the greatest ever year
loud music will be what you hear.

Bhavin Pandya (10)
Merton Court School

CELEBRATION 2000

We celebrate the millennium
once every one thousand years.
We love to have a party
and play and laugh and cheer.

When the clocks strike twelve
on December 1999,
the whole world
will be having a good time.

The Greenwich Dome
will be finished at last,
and all the bad memories
will be in the past.

Laurie Clode (11)
Merton Court School

My Party

If I had the opportunity
to have a millennium party,
I'd have it at the Highbury ground,
lots of joyful, happy sounds.

I'd have Arsenal and animals,
music and drink,
graffiti, confetti,
everyone dressed in pink.

That's what I'd do
if I had the opportunity
to have a millennium party.

Jody-Lan Castle (10)
Mundella CP School

The Year 2000

The year ends,
the new year begins.
The century ends,
the new century begins.
The millennium ends,
the new millennium begins.
The year of the Millennium Dome,
the year England win the Euro Cup,
the year I go to Grammar.
The year 2000.
Oh! Yes!

Simon Stuart (10)
Mundella CP School

WHAT SHOULD I DO?

Caribbean island is where I should be
for the millennium.
Yes, indeed!

Or maybe at theme parks, getting ill.
Up and down, round and round,
on the wheel.

Disco, parties, food and drink,
dancing, eating the night away.

Maybe up in Manchester at Old Trafford,
watching Man U play.

That's what I'll do in the millennium,
but now I'm just sitting at my desk,
watching the clock tick by.

Keep on hearing the world in my head,
millennium, millennium.

Lauren Staveley (10)
Mundella CP School

MILLENNIUM

Fireworks in the air,
Catherine wheels spin like mad,
rockets making colourful displays,
bangers going *bang! Kerboom!*
Jumping Jacks, jumping in the sky,
it's growing nearer,
it's almost here,
millennium!

Joe Chambers (9)
Mundella CP School

MILLENNIUM 2000

It's time for the millennium,
get your stuff together.
The clock has just struck twelve,
the whole of New York has just lit up
and fireworks are going bang.
People getting drunk at the pubs,
everybody at parties, my dad especially getting drunk.
My grandad falling off the kerb, I told him not to get drunk.
Everybody quiet at 11.59,
everybody silent,
then the clock struck twelve.
Everybody shouted,
'Millennium!'

Michael Ward (11)
Mundella CP School

MILLENNIUM

Stars shining brightly for the millennium,
shining far away in the clear, dark sky,
shooting across the universe.
Stars are for the new century,
for the millennium.

Stars are really planets shining,
very big and very bright,
like colourful fireworks.
Stars are bright,
stars are light,
stars travel around the world.

Gemma Atkins (10)
Mundella CP School

LOVE 2000

Millennium love,
will it blossom,
or will it die?

Millennium Bug,
will it start,
or will it stop?

Millennium Dome,
will it open,
or will it shut?

Millennium peace,
will you be friends?
It's a new millennium,
go on!

Daniel Bail (10)
Mundella CP School

MILLENNIUM

M illennium
I s when the excitement starts.
L ights all over the place,
L ighting up the towns and cities,
E very thousand years.
N ew animals appear.
N ineteen ninety-nine is here.
I t's the best in the world.
U p in the air balloons are there,
M illennium.

Natasha Spearpoint (9)
Mundella CP School

MILLENNIUM BUG

Millennium Bug
takes a bite from all the computers,
causing havoc.
TVs go bust,
but the Bug hasn't stopped
the party of the year 2000.

Kirk Beasley (11)
Mundella CP School

ALIENS

A liens are going to come to Earth!
L anding in your garden!
I nternet - new Internet.
E njoy the fun and party,
N asty aliens destroying the place!
S orry everyone, that probably won't happen!

Joshua Johnson (10)
Mundella CP School

THE VIOLENT STORM

Trees were swaying in the wind.
The shed roof was sliding.
Flowers drooping like fallen
trees in the woods.
Violent wind whistling,
water bucketing down in great anger,
clashing and banging on the windows.

Alex Bragg (9)
Northbourne Park School

THE STORM OF 1987

The wind howled around the house, hurtling in every direction.
The storm then broke out, more violently than ever.
The house seemed to move and we were afraid.
Then *bang!*
Lightning and thunder crashed.
The wind swept up,
Next creaking, groaning,
Then a tear and the roof had gone.
We were now under the powers of the skies,
Huddled together,
Keeping warm.
The house seemed to float and wing in the wind.
Windows rattled and broke, we sat there,
Shivering and afraid.

Aaron Kent (10)
Northbourne Park School

STORMY DAY

S tormy day, loud and fierce,
T errified by the thunder.
O utside, another of those windy days.
R ough seas and dangerous winds.
M y house has nearly been crushed I think.
Y elling thunder, it's terrifying.

D ancing winds and hailing rain,
A nd yet I quite enjoy it, but suddenly
Y elling storm calms down, the sun comes out and shines.

Oliver Ford (10)
Northbourne Park School

Tornado

The storm rushing through the village,
booming sounds on the moors,
houses battered by the terrible winds.
People staggering in the streets.
Tossing waves splashing over the sea walls,
flooding down the streets.
Roaring wind is deafening.
Windows shattering.
Rain stampeding the gardens.
Waves gathering for one huge splash,
violent winds howling outside.
Telegraph poles flying through the air.
People screaming.
Houses being crushed.
Sky is black and yellow.
Wind's teeth banging on people's doors.
Rubble all over the road.
Blazing fire burning trees.
Uprooted trees everywhere
and then, all is calm.

Theo Dunay (10)
Northbourne Park School

STORMS

Storms, thumping my roof and
stampeding the walls,
rocking the house, making me terrified,
full of fear, my heart beating.
Trees cracking,
the howling of dogs and the roar
of thunder and lightning.
I could see the brightness strike into the sky.
Solid white lightning striking the ground,
trees were violently tossing.

Richard Gould (10)
Northbourne Park School

FIRE

The fire is blazing.
A spit that explodes into yellow, orange light
and suddenly falls into darkness,
as if by a flicker has faded,
and then the burning begins.
The wood shrivels up and all in vain
it burns, it burns, it burns, until all is silent.
Nothing to be heard, for the fire is dead.

Daniel Hurley (10)
Northbourne Park School

THE MAGIC BOX

I put a ray of the sun in the box,
along with a spark of a firework
and a purple cloud went in, like a flash.

As I look at the box,
the shiny, gold lid catches my attention,
with the silver edges and the unicorn on the front.
Beautiful!

Next a diamond from a treasure chest,
then a violet dragon that breaths out pink candyfloss.
Afterwards, the bark of the oldest tree in the world,
and last of all, the roar of a lion.

The box was made out of
silver, gold, bronze and brass,
very heavy, but useful.
It always catches my attention.

With my box, I will fly around the world,
go sailing with it
and play with it everywhere.
I will never be lonely.

Susannah Fox (9)
Northbourne Park School

The Storm

A house all on its own behind some trees,
the rain pounding,
jumping off the house.
We looked at the blazing fire.
People staggered along outside,
bins tossing and turning, leaving the lids behind.
Clouds moving very fast,
so the storm will pass quickly.
Clouds leaping through the sky,
crashes of thunder getting closer to us,
wind howling through the windows.
I went to my room and sat frightened on my bed,
just waiting for the final crash of thunder.

James Stiles (10)
Northbourne Park School

The Storm

Squalls of sounds nearing towards us,
millions of them,
murmuring sounds flexing, gathering.
The wind crashing and booming loudly,
frightening screams of lightning.
The stormy thunder hammers down,
always groaning out loud.
As the storm approaches and the wind gathers speed,
it enters around the doors in the house,
howling, whistling.
Eventually dawn approaches,
it fades with the storm.

Edward Barker (9)
Northbourne Park School

SHOULD WE SAVE THE PLANET

An over-heating greenhouse,
toxic fumes destroying Earth,
no ozone layer to protect us.
The creatures God told us to protect
are dying because of us.
Should we save the planet?

Wars raging between humans.
Millions die for petty differences,
happy families are split up.
People kill their brothers
all because they are different colours.
Should we save the planet?

Loving families still survive,
beautiful birds fly through the toxic skies,
amazing creatures swim through the seas.
Animals move through the forests,
which humans cannot have noticed.
Perhaps we should save the planet!

Jack Lambert (12)
Northbourne Park School

AUTUMN

I stood looking up into the trees,
orange, red, yellow and brown all blended into one.
The skies full of twittering birds,
all chirping and fluttering.
The breeze blowing my hair
and the leaves crackling under my feet.

Elizabeth Ferrar (9)
Northbourne Park School

THE TERRIBLE NIGHT

The wind was howling on the window,
banging on the door.
The sky turned black,
clouds took over the sky,
covering the moon in less than three seconds.
Suddenly, a thunderous crash and a blinding flash of light.
It felt as if the house was moving.
The lights started to flicker as the wires quivered
and the ground trembled under my feet.
The wind was whistling outside.
The trees were being tossed about by the wind
and the sea was flooding the land.
The surf was almost up to my house.
I didn't dare to open the window, let alone go outside.

Samantha Jones (10)
Northbourne Park School

THE STORM

The storm crying outside,
the wind howling to get in,
it batters the house, while the
thunder stampedes outside.
The clouds march up and
down the sky.
When it stops, the sky turns
orange, it calms.

Adam Pickett (9)
Northbourne Park School

EMPTINESS

Emptiness is nothing.
Nothing is emptiness.
Emptiness means nothing is there,
like a jam jar, without jam
like a street with no houses.
If the world was full of emptiness,
then nothing would be there.

Sometimes people are full of emptiness,
normally through love, hate or despair.
Sometimes through doubt,
sometimes through loneliness.
If a person is full of the nothingness
of emptiness,
then the person is full of nothing at all.

Emptiness is nothing,
nothing is emptiness.
If the world wasn't full of anything,
then nothing would be there.

Robin Bailey (13)
Northbourne Park School

IN THE NEW MILLENNIUM

In sight of the new millennium, I can see the bitter sight of the petrol cars zooming along the road. They should have been wiped out long ago but nothing's changed much.

In the taste of the new millennium, I can taste a little pill that tastes of roast beef. The real beef became burned long ago, nothing's changed much.

In the sound of the new millennium, I can hear a tinkle of my robot as it comes and brings me my breakfast in bed. Nothing's changed much.

In the feel of the millennium, I can feel a change in poor countries. An international committee provides food for them but they are doing that already, so nothing's changed much.

In the smell of the new millennium, I can smell the smoke from a forest fire. Animals are screeching and people are dying, exhausted by the clouds of smoke. Nothing's changed much.

In the hopes of the new millennium, there will be no schools, instead there will be a free syringe which is full of a fluid that gives you all the knowledge you want. So at least something will change.

James A Sinclair (9)
St Andrew's Preparatory School, Edenbridge

IN THE NEW MILLENNIUM

In the sound of the new millennium I can hear the cogs
grinding and the electricity whizzing round the robots.
In the sight of the new millennium I can see bubble cars
whooping on fresh air leaving a trail of marshmallows behind them.

In the taste of the new millennium I can taste the bubblegum-flavoured
chocolate, sweet and tender on your tongue.
In the touch of the new millennium I can feel the silver, steel,
metal bars of my house laid neatly in lines.

In the feel of the new millennium I can feel technology and
electricity, robots, computers and systems for everything.
In the dream of the new millennium I can feel peace and hope.
Warmth and comfort for everyone.

Emily Hart (8)
St Andrew's Preparatory School, Edenbridge

MILLENNIUM

The millennium is coming,
With new inventions,
New information,
And new creations.
We will be able to explore space,
Maybe we will be able to meet some aliens!
People will have flying boots,
And roller-skates on stilts.
People will rejoice,
And champagne bottles will be spraying,
Everyone will shout,
The millennium,
Hurrah!

Soon another 1000 years will have passed,
The millennium will be here at last,
The world will join together,
And help each other,
New medicines will be found,
There will be no illnesses in the land,
Everything will look grand
When the millennium comes.

Helen Ritchie (9)
St Andrew's Preparatory School, Edenbridge

Millennium

The millennium is here, time to
Celebrate, get the party hats out
Get in the mood to celebrate
Turn the music on because
The millennium is here.

Since the last millennium things
Have changed, our intelligence
Has grown.

We have new machines, new ideas
A new world.

This millennium might have
New inventions perhaps we have
Grown more courageous since
The last millennium.

Joshua Kaufmann (10)
St Andrew's Preparatory School, Edenbridge

I Don't Like It

In the sound of the new millennium
I can't hear any birds singing, they have been
Killed by the pollution in the fields.
I don't like it.

In the sight of the new millennium
I can see war all over the the world
Bombs are being dropped on every country.
I don't like it.

In the smell of the new millennium
I can smell the car fumes out in the
Town, it is horrible to go out.
I don't like it.
In the taste of the new millennium
I can't taste the fresh vegetables and fruit
Nothing is fresh anymore.
I don't like it.

Phillippa Woolard (9)
St Andrew's Preparatory School, Edenbridge

A LONG WAY TO COME

A nother thousand years mankind has been alive.

L ove and kindness we've tried to show,
O ther difficulties have been in the way.
N o one can stop time so we're
G oing to live through the millennium.

W here we go nobody knows,
A nother solar system may be found.
Y ears have passed, 2000 to be precise.

T ogether we can make the world better,
O bstinate wars could end.

C elebrations all round the world,
O pportunities to rejoice!
M illennium is here, so party, and hope,
E veryone is happy and loved.

Glenn Masson (9)
St Andrew's Preparatory School, Edenbridge

THE NEW MILLENNIUM

In the new millennium I can hear
no song of the birds, not even the sparrows,
they have all been shot with poisoned arrows.

I can see in the new millennium
people visiting Mars
in their brightly-coloured speedy cars.

In the new millennium I can see
no rainforest or woods
just people with loads of fancy goods.

In the new millennium I can see
lazy children who have forgotten how to play.
All they do is eat all day.

In the new millennium I can dream
for peace and books and real ice-cream
and no need for police.

Rachel Pickford (9)
St Andrew's Preparatory School, Edenbridge

THE FUTURE

In the sound of the future, the electronic bird sings.
No thrush, no robin, no birdsong of old
Just the sound of an electronic buzz.
It's not like the old days at all.

In the sight of the future the space cars zoom out into space,
Leaving a luminous green trail behind them.
No petrol, no fuel, they just run on air.
It's not like the old days at all.

In the taste of the future the pills are so delicious,
No cheese, no bread, just different-flavoured pills.
It's not like the old days at all.

In the dreams of the future there will be no nightmares,
No ghosts in your sleep, no vampires to creep,
Just lovely relaxing dreams.
It's not like the old days at all.

Rose Hunnam (9)
St Andrew's Preparatory School, Edenbridge

LET'S CELEBRATE

The clock struck twelve,
Let's celebrate!
The past millennium,
Just think of all the people
Who have lived through the millennium,
And transformed it, changed it for all mankind.
They may have invented a fantastic device,
Or somehow changed society,
But think of them memorably.

The clock struck twelve,
Let's celebrate!
The new millennium,
Lots of fun for everyone.
Always strive to do your best,
During the new millennium.
The millennium could unite men and alien-kind,
No pollution, or acid rain, or forest fires,
How different the new millennium could be!

Georgina Wells (10)
St Andrew's Preparatory School, Edenbridge

IN THE NEW MILLENNIUM

In the new millennium I can hear the robots bleeping.
In the new millennium I can taste candy powder yoghurt.
In the new millennium I can see children learning
on their computers.
In the new millennium I can feel the soft clouds as I
fall to sleep.
In the new millennium I can watch the world go by
from my floating bubble car.
In the new millennium I listen to the quiet of capable machines
as they go about their work.
In the new millennium no cries of sick and pain.
In the new millennium clean air comes again.
In the new millennium it is going to be alright after all.

Lauren Prewer (10)
St Andrew's Preparatory School, Edenbridge

MY WORLD 2000

My world 2000 would be great,
So come on people let's celebrate.
The millennium's a time for joy,
And hope for every girl and boy.

We celebrate this wonderful day,
With parties, food and friends to stay.
No more fighting please, please,
I beg on my knees
No more fighting please please.

Lewis Noble (9)
St Andrew's Preparatory School, Edenbridge

NO MORE

The buzzing of the space car is here,
Most wildlife has gone.
The robots come and go,
Buzz, buzz and they are gone.

The world is like a giant jungle,
Electronic birds do sing.
The whirr, whirr of the big cat,
Roar, roar and he is gone.

No more nuclear warheads
All wars have been and gone.
Peace rules, peace rules.
But it's not all that good, read on.

No birds are left to sing,
No flowers are left to bloom.
The engineers died to bring them back,
But their spirit still lives on.

Everything is computerised.
Fat lazy children in front of the dreaded screen.
Computers, computers.
Their demands are so mean.

Tom Jennings (8)
St Andrew's Preparatory School, Edenbridge

CELEBRATION 2000

We will celebrate all night long,
Blazing fireworks will colour the sky,
All of the world will celebrate,
The sky of golden stars will turn the sky
Blue, red, yellow and green.

We celebrate our ancestors who have
Given to us the freedom of living our
Lives the way we want to,
I think the year 2000 will be a time of
Joy, happiness and peace.

Everyone around the world will celebrate,
The Russians will sing their songs,
The Chinese will write their stories,
The Arabians will turn their towns into
Bright shining cities.

We celebrate our millennium for all of the
Wonderful inventors,
We celebrate the millennium because of all the
Things that have taken place,
We also celebrate for the courageous people
Who have hoped for great things in the world.

Seán Hickey (9)
St Andrew's Preparatory School, Edenbridge

REJOICE

Celebration for the nation
Get celebrating for the nation.
Celebration for a nation, a party
Get celebrating for the nation.

It is 2000

My celebration for 2000,
Will be full of fun,
From men leaping from place to place,
To funny men juggling with fire.
So rejoice, it's 2000.

Milton Cato (10)
St Andrew's Preparatory School, Edenbridge

THE NEW MILLENNIUM

In the new millennium the birds are singing nursery rhymes
they have learnt to speak in human language.
Everything has changed.

In the new millennium there are no petrol-driven cars,
all transport is shaped like bubbles which you blow up before a journey.
Everything has changed.

In the new millennium there is only perfumed air that smells like lime.
Everything has changed.

In the new millennium I can taste flowers which have
petals made out of sherbet, and the middle of them is
made out of marshmallow.
Everything has changed.

In the new millennium I watch TV on my wrist watch
and do school work on my computer
Everything has changed.

In the new millennium I can dream about the past,
when they went to school and learnt about the future.
The future is us!
That has changed!

Sophie Armitage (9)
St Andrew's Preparatory School, Edenbridge

The Millennium

In the sound of the new millennium
I can hear the buzzing of the electric hover cars.

In the smell of the new millennium
I can smell no fuel, no pollution and no smoke.

In the sight of the new millennium
I can see peace and kindness.

In the taste of the new millennium
I can taste pills of roast lamb and crisp flavoured bubblegum.

In the feel of the new millennium
I can feel a good life, hope and no more wars.

In the dream of the new millennium
I dream that everybody eats good food, has clean water,
TVs, schools and clean, safe homes.

Henry Croft (9)
St Andrew's Preparatory School, Edenbridge

Medusa

Slithery snakes of hair will give you a shocking scare,
Those piercing eyes that turn you to stone,
Will make you groan with sadness,
But if you fight brave and strong and behead the evil gorgon,
Pegasus the winged horse will rise and present you with
a rewarding prize.

Siân Bolton (10)
St Eanswythe School, Folkestone

CYCLOPS

When you go by don't wake him,
when you go by be very, very brave.
Be careful that you don't fall in his traps
or he will get you and go snap snap.
        The evil Cyclops.

The evil red eye is shining bright,
and if you go into his kingdom
you'll get a horrible fright.
        The evil Cyclops.

If you steal any gold or silver,
you will get a horrible shiver.
        The evil Cyclops.

He has horrible breath that will
give you an evil death and if you are
looking for gold you will get hidden in bones.
        The evil Cyclops.

Cyclops is an evil man
his eye can turn you into a frying pan.
        The evil Cyclops.

Chantelle Marsh (9)
St Eanswythe School, Folkestone

Golden Owl Will Come Again

The owl sat branching in a tree,
Scanning the ground mercilessly.
Its delicate feathers each gold,
And if one would fall away,
By looking at the sun's ray,
The owl would die so it is told.

The owl had a son of his own.
Same plumage had he but unknown.
Except the father who told none.
Foolish was he not to tell,
For his son's life he would sell,
By him looking at the cruel sun.

The story starts in early morn.
The owlet woken by a horn.
He wanted to follow the sound.
He followed the loud cry,
Till he heard it from the sky.
Feathers floated from all around.

Now dead was the father's young heir.
The father's life they could not spare,
For he tried to stop the poor bird,
But he himself faced the sun.
Now the golden owls were none.
No more gold owls ever heard.

And now owls always wake at night.
And to keep their sons always in sight,
Their eyes will always be bigger.
A gold egg will come a day.
A golden owl so they say.
When that day is we can't figure.

Golden owl will come
Again.

Josie Bryant (10)
St Eanswythe School, Folkestone

MY LITTLE BROTHER

My little brother drives me up the wall.
When I want to talk to him I have to call and call.
He looks cute in his glasses,
But when it comes to manners he needs classes.
When I'm watching TV he does nothing but talk,
But when it comes to shopping he certainly won't walk.
When I do my homework all he does is play.
And when it comes to bedtime *'No'* is all he'll say.
My little brother is four years old,
And already he is worth his weight in *gold.*

Terri Hines (10)
St Eanswythe School, Folkestone

The Magic Box

I will squash in my box . . .
a soothing scarlet sunset which has a taste of chilli,
over a scented meadow full of horses
galloping around like rockets.

I will cram in my box . . .
constant pockets of love, posted by God Almighty
also my loving family and caring friends.

In one corner of my box . . .
I'd have a chocoroom,
where there would be drawers full of chocolate.

I'd let float into my box . . .
Thirty beautiful herbs to give my box a unique smell
and my favourite band Bewitched
playing gently in the background.

I will decorate my box . . .
with fresh water-coloured blue paint,
golden sparkling stars on the lid and the base.
Hand-painted murals of Forever Friends on the lid.

Jade Underdown (11)
St Eanswythe School, Folkestone

Aliens

A liens with glowing eyes,
L eering and staring at you,
I nnocently but truthful,
E xcept for its mind it thinks wrong all the time,
N othing on the whole Earth lives in space except for the aliens,
S wallowing pieces of our planet as it goes.

Devi Patel
St Eanswythe School, Folkestone

THE MINOTAUR

Beware of the minotaur's lair,
As you walk in there,
He may be in there.

Grasp your sword in hand,
Then prepare for battle,
He'll be waiting with all his hating,
So don't keep him waiting.

He hits you with his claw,
Knocks you to the floor,
He gives a tremendous roar.

The look in his eyes could kill,
The horns on his head could pierce your skull,
The teeth in his mouth could grind you to flour,
His claws have so much power.

He throws you to the ground,
With his hands he begins to pound,
You get up from the ground.

You discover a knife,
Take it in hand,
Aim the knife at his heart
Then take his life.

You now are free to do whatever you want,
You've won the war against the minotaur.

Christopher Croucher (11)
St Eanswythe School, Folkestone

THE WIZARD

As the wizard mixed his brew
Silently he went all blue
He shouted out in a silly voice 'glue'
That's what I'll do

The next few days
With his wizardly ways
Made a thing called glue
He said 'I'll put some berries
And a little cup of cherries
And some little tiny fairies.'

The king had commanded the wizard
To create something to mend the castle gate
If he did not do it he would meet a nasty fate.
The wizard did not want to lose his head
That's why he had worked hard to make a spell
And now thank goodness things were going well.

He walked through the castle
And delivered his parcel
And ran home as quick as he could
By the next morning thoughts were dawning upon him
That the spell might have worked
A man rushed to the door with a warning.
The King's men were here for him.

The King congratulated him
And sounded sort of dim
Thank goodness he could keep his head.

Charles Brisley (11)
St Eanswythe School, Folkestone

THE DRAGON

It flies, it's alive, the evil in its eyes.
It scratches, it bites, it has no one to like.
It has two heads, but only one bed.
It flies higher, breathes out fire.
Its long long tail, swish, swail.
Its big claws, on huge paws.
Its back spikes, ouch, yikes.
Needs to be caught.
It's trouble
Oh no.
Help!

Patricia Plested (10)
St Eanswythe School, Folkestone

HUNTING IN WINTER

As the echoes surround my ears,
They make me drink my most rounded beer.
I walk all day in the snow,
With my arrow and my bow.
I shot a deer with my arrow,
But I missed and hit a marrow.
I picked the marrow up,
In the world's most beautiful cup.
We made marrow stew,
And we had not a clue.
The next morning,
The rain was pouring,
So the ducks enjoyed it,
But we mourned it!

Charles Henry Player (10)
St Ronan's School, Hawkhurst

Approaching 2000

The year is approaching,
The everlasting feeling,
Of being split in half,
Your life in two centuries,
Two millenniums,
The unknown minds of those who built the world,
Now what miraculous discoveries we will find.
Maybe a new beginning on the moon,
Find our long-lost neighbours,
The evolution of men and nature,
Carries on through the millennium,
The evolution of discovery and invention,
This is a time of celebration,
What crowds shall gather in Time Square,
But only to see the semantic motion of time,
Moving on like it has for the past billions of years,
Everyone in a great rhythm,
In happiness,
For the new millennium.

James Merewether (13)
St Ronan's School, Hawkhurst

The Ting Tan Ton

On the ting tan ton where
The trees all go pon and the sheep all go baa.
There's a tan ton ting
Where the cows go bing and the
Tea pots go jibber jabber joo.
There's a place called the coo-coo
And in the coo-coo you do all kinds of things
Like see kangaroos and see a hoppercoo.

Michelle Faure (7)
St Ronan's School, Hawkhurst

FISHES

F ast and sleek in the water deep,
I n the dark blue depths of the sea,
S ome small exotic salmon leap,
H addock hunt and small minnows flee,
E xotic fish propel themselves in front,
S o swift with scaly skin,

I dle fishermen, soaking up the sun,
N othing happening in the fishing hunt,

T oxic barrels and waste from a bin,
H elpless fish once look what man has done,
E ach fish has a different colour,

S ome as black as night, which makes you shudder,
E ager all to get some tea,
A ll in the dark blue depths of the sea.

Alexander Graham (11)
St Ronan's School, Hawkhurst

TIGER

Stripy and strong
The tiger stomps in the grass.
He pants!
It is very hot!
He is looking for his prey.
The tiger has seen a deer,
Then he pounces on it,
Then jumps up into a tree
And goes to sleep.

Rupert Tozer (7)
St Ronan's School, Hawkhurst

THE SEA FISHES

The very fathomless and sapphire sea.
I see the bright exotic colours of the fish.
Some fish are harsh.
Other fish are generous.

The sea can be calm and can be rough.
The different boats sailing boats.
There are transport boats as well.
The waves, the fish.

The sea is just beautiful.
People go diving in the sea.
To examine what is hidden under the waters.
They examine fish to know more about them.

What a shame to see fishing boats destroying life.
Under the dark blue waters.
No one knows what is under the waters
Until you have been there.

There are sharks which are harsh.
There are dolphins which are generous.
That is the fathomless and sapphire sea.

Anthony Drewe (13)
St Ronan's School, Hawkhurst

KITTEN

My ginger kitten has very small meals.
When he goes to the beach,
He runs from the seals.

He likes catching mice,
But when it comes to feeding,
Don't feed him rice.
(It's because he's allergic to it.)

He has very fuzzy furry paws,
But you'd better watch out,
He has very sharp claws.

One of his eyes is brown,
While the other is blue.
When he jumps off the table,
It looks like he flew.

Jonathan Langer (8)
St Ronan's School, Hawkhurst

I Hate Being Nine

I am nine give me a sign
But I still whinge and whine
Everything is mine
(but I still don't like being nine)

I'm doing really badly at school
I accidentally fell in the pool
I don't like writing
But I do like fighting
(and I really hate being nine)

I have built a den
Near a wren
I built a fort
And in a battle I fought
I had been taught
To build a fort
(I'm looking forward to being ten).

Edward Prest (8)
St Ronan's School, Hawkhurst

TIGER, TIGER

Tiger, tiger,
Cunning stripes,
With a heart blazing out loud,
Consuming his body into a
Time-stalking, dangerous
Beautiful creature.
How has thou taken his image,
Creating a mastery of the legend,
When the Lord poured down,
Holy water from the sky,
His tears from his eye,
Burning thy spirit
Into a tiger's soul.
God rolled down a tooth of his,
Casting a mystical spell,
Of cunning, beautiful, wise and danger
Into the eye of a tiger.
Tiger, tiger, o tiger
When will thou come out?
To show the cries upon the highs,
Of the cities of men.
Showing the wisdom
Of knowing what mankind has done.

Tom Helm (10)
St Ronan's School, Hawkhurst

MY DADDY IS FAT

Once upon a time my daddy was very fat
But he did exercise and got very thin
And was never greedy again.

Richard Blundell (6)
St Ronan's School, Hawkhurst

THE FINAL

Today is the day of the final,
I drift about in drowsy sleep,
Until my dad comes in to rouse me,
And says 'Come downstairs to have breakfast and get dressed.'
Soon I had done all he asked,
And I strapped myself into the car,
To set off towards the football pitch,
Half an hour later I find myself by the pitch,
Wearing the Cranbrook kit.
Standing next to my team mates and listening to the manager talk,
Today I'm playing from the start,
And I nervously wait for the kick off.
Soon we're playing in full flow.
The opposition is tough,
But our team is even with their team,
And as time goes by it's nil-nil,
As the referee blows his whistle to signal the end of the match,
My team mate Sam kicks the ball,
And it flies into the back of the net.
The referee ends his blow,
And we suddenly realise we won.
My team mates, manager, parents and I,
Taste the sweet taste of victory,
And sing ourselves all the way home.

Donal MacCrann (11)
St Ronan's School, Hawkhurst

TIGER

Stripy and fierce
It pants.
It pounces on a deer.
To her cubs
She stumps
Along the grass
To the wild wood.
Along comes a herd of deer.
She pounces on one
But she isn't hungry.
She eats with the cubs.
Her stomach is full.
She falls asleep.
She wakes up in the morning.

Harry Hoblyn (7)
St Ronan's School, Hawkhurst

THE DUCK

The duck eating fish,
And he says quack quack quack.
The duck can fly and swim.
His feathers are green and brown.
In the autumn
He flies two thousand miles
Because he doesn't want to die,
In the snow.
He must find food and warmth
To survive.
And when they fly, somebody is hunting them.

Alex Kelin (9)
St Ronan's School, Hawkhurst

THE POLAR BEAR

The polar bear sleeps
Until he is hungry
Then slowly he gets up.
Then suddenly, he goes
Out of the cave.
He walks to the water.
He feels it,
Then he jumps
Into the water.
He goes underwater,
Then gets ready to eat a fish.
He opens his mouth.
He shuts it.
He has got it in his mouth.
Then he swims
Up to the surface
And goes to his cave
And sleeps again.

Geoffrey Woodman (7)
St Ronan's School, Hawkhurst

MONKEY

Brown and smooth
The monkey moves quickly
He eats fruit
But he must pick the fruit
From a tree he can climb
So high only a few can see him
He can climb so quickly
Like a dash of lightning in the trees.

Oliver Marshall (7)
St Ronan's School, Hawkhurst

My Cat

My cat is very lazy.
He is very greedy, purrs a lot.
He is called Michael.
He is black and white.
He has very sharp claws.
He runs very fast.
He is very silly.
He has very soft fur.
He miaows a lot.
I love him very much.
He likes catching mice and rabbits.
I always see him when I get home.
When he goes out he just comes back in.
He always sits on my bed.

Ralph Johnson (8)
St Ronan's School, Hawkhurst

Teachers

Teachers are features
Such features there are,
The features of teachers
Don't go very far!
They're mean
And they're nasty
And ghastly
Sometimes fun
For playing
Tricks on one.

Andrew Denman (8)
St Ronan's School, Hawkhurst

DRUNK JAMES

James was drunk
Glunk! Glunk! Glunk!
He drank and drank
And got spanked and spanked

He looked very strange
Pink as a pig
And he grew small to big
He drank in jugs, cans and cups

And he drank beer and a little bit of deer
He was very fat as big as the cat
And was lying on a big big mat.

__Charlie Houghton (9)__
__St Ronan's School, Hawkhurst__

COPY FAMILY

Copy copy copy family
Baby: I read a book you read a book.
Kid: I spill some milk you spill some milk.
Mum: I'm a night nurse you are a night nurse.
Dad: I'm a teacher you are a teacher.
Family: We live in St Ronan's and you do.
But one thing which you don't is
Keep a giant octopus, dragon and unicorn

and a hundred other animals including 101 Dalmatians.

__Jonathan Clowes (8)__
__St Ronan's School, Hawkhurst__

STICKY STUFF STICKY STUFF

Sticky stuff! Sticky stuff!
All over your clothes
Put it in the washer
And hope it comes off
Take it out and find it's still there
Soak it for a year
Or put it in your ear

Sticky bubblegum I've got it on my clothes
My mum is cross
And my dad is mad
And I've nowhere to go but home

I was blowing a bubble
It burst on my sweater
It burst because
Of my brother
he poked it
With his big finger.

Bertie Blundell (8)
St Ronan's School, Hawkhurst

SEA

The glassy and watery sea,
clashing against the rocks,
tossing and turning everywhere,
bashing on the coast.

The sea is my friend,
I like it a lot,
I collect all its wonders,
that have come from the deep.

I imagine all the mermen,
and the mermaids too,
I wish I could see them,
and all their wonderful things.

James Duval (9)
St Ronan's School, Hawkhurst

PUPPIES

Puppies
They are cute
They lick you
They bark a lot
Their coats are soft
They fall off tables, chairs

They are sweet
They become very excited
When they play with balls
I pick them up
I stroke them
They sleep on my bed
They like sticks

They run quickly! Fast!
Some are called Patchy
My puppy is called Patchy as well
Patchy is called Patchy, why?
He has got a patch on him.
I like puppies
What about you?

Alexander Macintyre (8)
St Ronan's School, Hawkhurst

A Dolphin

The dolphin is a friend to man
He plays with us
The dolphin can kill a shark
But he also eats fish
He is a fast swimmer
He is a mammal
Who lives in the sea
He is smooth and shiny
He is bluey grey
They are kind mothers
They are friends of people
I like dolphins
And the way they swim
And how they jump.

Alastair Borland (8)
St Ronan's School, Hawkhurst

The Man And The Cat

There was a man who lived in a van.
He had a cat who sat on a mat.
She had a fish who lay in a dish.
The man and the cat moved to a flat.
The man gave the cat a bit of the fish.
She bit it in half right in the dish.
When she had finished she went to the mat.
There she fell fast asleep.
When she woke up she went to the man.
She jumped on his knee.
Then they both fell asleep under the tree.

Phoebe Katis (6)
St Ronan's School, Hawkhurst

I AM SAD

I am sad because
my mum hit me with
a big elastic band.
I was rollerblading in the kitchen.
Mummy doesn't like it,
But I do!

Rupert Munro-Faure (6)
St Ronan's School, Hawkhurst

I WISH I HAD A PET GIRAFFE

I wish I had a pet giraffe
So I could knit a long long scarf
I wish I had a kangaroo
Perhaps a lion too!
Even though I think I'm lucky,
I have a brand new puppy!

Sarah Yelland (8)
St Ronan's School, Hawkhurst

THE GREEDY CAT

There was a fat greedy cat
He ate a lot of mice
He got fatter and fatter and didn't stop
Soon he popped and he looked like a thin bit of glass
So he only ate one mouse a day
And was never greedy ever again.

William Prest (6)
St Ronan's School, Hawkhurst

MY PUPPY

I have a cuddly puppy called Phoebe,
She is shiny black with huge paws,
Her ears are enormous too!
She eats her food madly,
She is a nice puppy.
She splashes water when she's drinking,
My puppy barks a lot,
She chases things,
She runs fast,
She is very jumpy,
She plays a lot,
She is bigger than my other dogs,
She is very heavy,
All my dogs want to go for a walk,
Phoebe is furry,
    I love my dogs.

Toby Walker (8)
St Ronan's School, Hawkhurst

THE KING AND QUEEN

Once there was a castle.
The queen and king sat in their chairs
Until the king thought and had an idea.
The king and queen went down the stairs
and opened the door.
They had a fight with some soldiers.
The king and queen won the fight
and then they had a feast.

Oliver Tozer (6)
St Ronan's School, Hawkhurst

TOFFEE

Toffee, toffee
You're wonderful stuff
I love you toffee
I can't get enough
You're covered with wrapping
And sprinkled with chocolate
Toffee, toffee
Oh, give me more please!

Anna Munro-Faure (9)
St Ronan's School, Hawkhurst

MY POCKET MONEY DAY

I am happy because it is my pocket money day.
I will fly to the moon and then come down again.
If I've got some money left I will say hello to a baboon.
I will go home and wait for my next pocket money day.

Victoria Yelland (6)
St Ronan's School, Hawkhurst

A PENCIL

A pencil can't write without a hand
A pencil can scribble and write and draw
If you draw for too long
You have to sharpen it again.

Jack Stow (6)
St Ronan's School, Hawkhurst

Millennium

It is the dawn of a new era,
The rapid change of our ways,
Greatest destruction and a new way of life,
The millennium brings forth hope.

The grandness of it holds no bounds,
No way to bring it to a halt,
It constantly edges closer through the vanishing days,
The millennium holds our future.

We will benefit deeply from it,
For many years to come,
It will prove to make us powered,
The millennium will kill us and birth us.

After one thousand years of waiting
The second looks even more prosperous
No one knows what it contains
The millennium, we hope, will guide us.

Soon two thousand years from the birth of our Lord,
Our ancestors and theirs go out of our sight,
The celebration will marvel,
The millennium brings cheers and songs of joy.

Hooray for the millennium,
Its destruction brings hope,
It's impossible to desist,
The millennium is what we shall live in.

Charlie Elias (13)
St Ronan's School, Hawkhurst

My Mum

My mum has curly hair
And she likes to dance like Cher.
My mum likes to drive her car,
And she goes very far.
My mum has shiny hair,
And she's very fair.
My mum has blue eyes,
And she likes to fly.
My mum wears her lipstick,
But sometimes she's a dipstick.
My mum smells like sunflowers,
Because she's got super powers.
My mum is nice,
Just like rice!

Samantha Miles (10)
Sandown CP School

Mum

My mum loves David Beckham.
If Man U don't win, she'll deck them.
She also loves Robbie Williams.
She's worth more than millions.
In her spare time she makes tables
And hates the smell of stables.
Eats lamb, potatoes and beans.
Wears jumpers and jeans.
She tells lots of jokes.
She never ever pokes.
I love my mum and she loves me.

Rebecca Crutchley (10)
Sandown CP School

My Future

Will we still have schools
Or will we sit at home?
Will there still be houses?

Will elephants still have two tusks
Or will they only have one?
Will tigers still be stripy?

Will the sea dry up
Or will it not?
Will fish still be alive?

Will astronauts still go to space?
Will we go to space for a holiday
Or will we not?

Matthew Larkins (9)
Sandown CP School

My Grandma

My grandma's getting old,
But she still helps in her cafe,
She's got short black curly hair,
Wears glasses and a cheerful smile.

She never wears trousers,
But wears silver nail varnish,
Smells of sweet perfume,
She's kind, helpful and listens.

She's my best friend.

Sonia Woolls (10)
Sandown CP School

My Dream Place

I dream of a place where I long to live always:
Big detached houses, a peaceful German village;

Gentle hills that roll along, green and colourful
The lovely balcony stands by the window ledge.

Fascinating views of the seven tranquil hills
Dreaming as I gaze over the garden hedge.

I look down at my vast and glorious garden
The massive, lily-filled pond has reeds at the edge.

I dream of a place where I long to be always
Rolling hills, my home, a peaceful German village.

Phillipa Engels (10)
Sandown CP School

Grumpy Grandad

Grandad is a guy who really smokes.
He has a bad right leg.
He has wrinkly hands with which he pokes.

I like him, don't get me wrong,
His leg he keeps out straight and long.
He loves reading, hence his glasses,
He's not a man who enjoys dances.
His greyish hair is losing colour,
He likes his stick, he wants no other.
Oh his creamed potatoes are lovely.

Ben Kelly (10)
Sandown CP School

My Grandmum

My grandmum is lovely,
She sings to me a lot,
And when I go to see her,
She shows me all the ornaments she's got.

We go and feed the birds together
And watch the seagulls fly.
There's a special bird called Gus
Who we watch fly by.

She has brown hair
And big brown eyes.
She prays to God
And never lies.

The only thing I don't like
Is that she never comes anywhere with us.
I don't blame her though,
We're always on a bus.

Jane Houldsworth (10)
Sandown CP School

My Future

M onsters may eat the universe
Y ou will be my friend.

F un may not be any more.
U nderground we may live.
T ime will be wasted on me.
U niverse may be gone.
R ain may never go away.
E ach planet may be gone.

Thomas Beach (9)
Sandown CP School

My Dream Place

I dream of a place where I long to live always:
Clear sea, warm breeze and over-turning waves.

The crimson sunset shines through the land,
While people walk along the yellow sand.

Crawling crabs scatter on the rocks,
Splashing whales swim through the water.

The sound of clashing stones and rocks echoes in my ear
Then I take a walk along the big white pier.

The shining shells sitting on the shore,
Gliding seagulls flutter through the air.

Sophie Barrow (10)
Sandown CP School

My Future

Will there be
A world war three?

Will there be
Pure air to breathe?
Will there still be buildings?

Will there be
Flying cars?
Will there still be the sea?

Will there be
Robots to help us?
Give us the answers.

Steven Curry (9)
Sandown CP School

My Future

Will there still be buildings
Or will we live on streets?
Will we still have schools?

Will there still be white rhinos
Or will they disappear?
Will dogs and cats still be pets or will
They be wild animals?

In the year two thousand
Will chimpanzees be wild
Or will they be like us?
Will the sea be there?

Will lions and tigers be pets
Or will they not?
Will the sea still be polluted
Or will it not?

Sam Richards (9)
Sandown CP School

My Cousin

My cousin is funny,
He likes dancing with me,

He jumps about like a bunny,
His favourite animal is a bee,

He likes to eat honey,
He likes to swim in the sea,

I wouldn't like another cousin,
I know he loves me.

Maria Letts (10)
Sandown CP School

MY FUTURE

Will the world still be here
Or will the air be clean?
Will we have a globe around us
Or will we have flying cars
Or will they run on the sun?

What will the future be like?
I wonder where I'll be?
Will England still be here?

I wonder what the millennium will be like?
Will the animals live to see it
Or will they be extinct?
Will we have a visit from some aliens?
Will mankind be extinct?

Will the dinosaurs be alive?
Will they rule the world?
What will the millennium be like?
It will, it will be a surprise.

Alex Riley (9)
Sandown CP School

MY FUTURE

Will it all be dark?
Will the moon explode
Or will it stay where it is?

Will dinosaurs come back?
Will cars disappear
Or will cars fly?

Daniel Stenhouse (9)
Sandown CP School

My Future

In the next millennium will people live on Mars?
What will happen to modern-day cars?
Will there be no more endangered species?
Will we find more human-like species?
What will the world be worth?

Will there be schools or outdoor pools?
Will the sea expand?
Will there be less land?
What will the world be worth?

Will robots and aliens command and take over all land?
Will the Millennium Dome be a huge home?
What will the world be worth?

Will aliens have holidays on Earth?
Will we be able to talk straight after birth?
Will the sunlight be blocked out or will there
Still be a yearly drought?
What will the world be worth?

Will the Earth be round?
Will humans live in a pound?
Will dinosaurs exist?
I can't write it all it's such a long list!
So what will the world be worth?

Sam Hutchings (9)
Sandown CP School

My Future

Will we go on holiday in space
Or will we stay at home?
Will we go to Pluto,
Mars or Venus on holiday?

Will we live in a dome on Mercury?
Will we have homes to live in
Or live on the cold and dusty streets?
Our homes are nice and warm.

Tim Pitcher (9)
Sandown CP School

MY FUTURE

Will people talk to animals
Or will dinosaurs come back?
Will animals die out
Or will the number of animals grow?

Will the Millennium Dome fall down,
Or will it stand up very high?
Will another dome be built,
Or will this dome be the only one?

Will astronauts live in space,
Or will they just live on Earth?
Will an air dome be built on the moon,
Or will the moon be destroyed?

Will robots do all the work
Or will they take over the Earth?
Will people stop being born,
Or will they carry on forever?

Will medicines stop being made
Or will they keep being made?
Will seas be cleaner,
Or will they still be polluted?

Joseph Douglas (9)
Sandown CP School

My Future

Will there be grass in Egypt?
Will Egypt have more pyramids?
Will Egypt have more beaches?

Will astronauts live in space?
If they did they could see other planets
Will they like it?

Will there be pollution in the sea?
Will the sea turn to ice?
Will the sea turn colour?

Neil Jackson (9)
Sandown CP School

My Future

M any years ago, when dinosaurs did survive
I n years gone by, many animals came along
L ast dinosaurs came to an end
L ater the animals came along
E ve came along and so did Adam
N ever will man not live, I hope
N ew ideas, new hopes
I wonder what the future holds
U nexpected people, coming, knocking at the door
M agic overtakes us all, or will it?

Holly Newing (9)
Sandown CP School

My Future

Will there be
a world war three?
Will there be computers
to teach?

Will there be
flying cars?
Will the sea be there?

Will robots be
servants?
Will the air be clean?

Will there be a city on Mars?
Will the Earth
be invaded by aliens?

Simon Love (9)
Sandown CP School

My Future

Will dinosaurs come back?
Will we still be alive?
What will the Earth be?

Will aliens discover the world?
Will animals survive?
What will the millennium bug do?

Will the grass be green?
Will the air be clean?
Will we survive?

Emma Lawless (9)
Sandown CP School

My Hope

Will the grass be green?
Will the air be clean?
Will there still be animals?
Will the clouds go by?
Will there still be people?
Will there still be cars?
Will the trees die?
Will there still be woods?
Will the water be blue?
Will the boats be new?

Ben Stevens (9)
Sandown CP School

My Future

Will astronauts still go to space?
Will there be people living on the moon?
Will there be more planets in our solar system?
I do not have a clue, do you?
Will there be more games?
Will the sea and air be clean?
Will the moon be bigger?
Will it snow every year?
Will there still be animals?

Cai Martin (9)
Sandown CP School

MY FUTURE

Will there be cities under seas?
Will there be bugs or fleas?
Will there be more wild cats?
Will there be poisonous rats?

Will there be any schools?
Will people use their tools?
Will there be the seven seas?
Will there be buzzing bees?

Will people still live on Earth?
Will babies have their birth?
Will there be dinosaurs?
Will there be any laws?

Will there be pies, apples and pears?
Will there be wild bears?
Will there be apple pies?
Will there be stormy skies?

Matthew Robinson (9)
Sandown CP School

I HOPE

I hope the aliens come down
I hope I go to Mars
I hope I go to Charlie's chocolate factory
I hope cars will fly
I hope there will be more food
I hope there will be more books to read.

Jon Stones (9)
Sandown CP School

My Future

Will there still be cars
Or will they disappear?
Who knows if they will?
Not me, not you, not anyone.

Will the millennium turn out good?
Do you think it will?
Who knows if it will?
Not me, not you, not anyone.

Will we have to work all day
Or will the teachers disappear?
Who knows if they will?
Not me, not you, not anyone.

Will the millennium still have houses
Or will we live in space?
Hope we don't live in space
Who knows if we will?
Not me, not you, not anyone.

Vicky Smith (9)
Sandown CP School

My Hope

I hope I can speak to animals
I hope the sea will be clean
I hope the world will be rich
And the aliens will come to see
I hope there are more schools
So poor people can learn.

Thomas Best (10)
Sandown CP School

What Will My Future Be Worth

What will my future be worth, be worth?
What will my future be worth?
Will we still be alive?
Will white tigers still survive?

What will my future be worth, be worth?
What will my future be worth?
Will we still be using cars?
Will humans live on Mars?

What will my future be worth, be worth?
What will my future be worth?
How old will we live to be?
Will you still remember me?

What will my future be worth, be worth?
What will my future be worth?
Will robots roam the Earth?
Will we dance with glee and mirth?

What will my future be worth, be worth?
What will my future be worth?
What will happen at the millennium?
Will babies still feed from their mum?

What will my future be worth, be worth?
What will my future be worth?
Will seas still be clean?
Will fields still be green?

Laura Skelton (9)
Sandown CP School

My Future

Will the teacher disappear
Or go to another planet?
In the class.

Will the school have science
All the time in the millennium
Or people stop being naughty?

Will the millennium have more houses
Or make the light go out?
No one knows.

Will my friend and I
Go to a friendly world?
I don't know and nobody knows.

Hannah Gearey (9)
Sandown CP School

My Future

Will there still be dinosaurs?
Will the sea be clean?
Will there still be pegasauruses
And will the peas be green?
Will mothers still have babies?
Will children still have clothes?
Will birds still have eggs
And will children still have bows?
Will the dogs still be pets
Or will they live in the farm?
Will your babies still be small
And will they fit in your arms?

Lisa Owen (9)
Sandown CP School